CYBORG—*Evolution of the Superman*

Books by the Same Author

COMPUTERS—*The Machines We Think With*
THE COMING AGE OF SOLAR ENERGY

CYBORG -

Evolution of the Superman

---

by D. S. Halacy, Jr.

HARPER & ROW PUBLISHERS · NEW YORK AND EVANSTON

FOR IRENE

LIBRARY OF CONGRESS CATALOG CARD NUMBER: 65–14673

C-R

Contents

Foreword by Manfred Clynes, D. Sc.   6
1   The Cyborg—and Why   9
2   Evolution to the Cyborg   22
3   Cyborg Revolution   36
4   The Human Machine   46
5   Artificial Outer Man   60
6   Artificial Inner Man   75
7   The Brain   91
8   Myoelectric Control   105
9   Drugs   118
10 Hypothermia   128
11 The Military Cyborgs   137
12 Cyborgs in Space   146
13 Tissue Culture   157
14 The Gene Tinkerers   173
15 Morality of the Cyborg   190
16 The Cyborg's Future   197
Index   203

Foreword

What is man? What will man become? That man should peren-
nially ask these questions and provide ever-new answers is an
indication of his being. Man is an individual but he is also an
element in the human community which makes possible many of
his greatest attributes—those like speech and science. Man is a
social being as well as a singing, dancing, reasoning mammal. The
growth of his individual relationship to the universe will be made
possible as much by the accumulation of *total* human capacity
through history as by the contribution of individual insight, fervor,
and knowledge.

Let us also remember our fundamental ignorance. Surprisingly,
perhaps, a proper awareness of this ignorance is one of the pro-
foundest elements of knowledge man is caable of. We talk readily
about magnetism, for instance, but in spite of its familiarity its
real nature is as much a mystery as is atomic energy, space, love,
or life itself. We can operate successfully with magnetism, but
understand it we cannot. We can merely accept it. What we call
forces in nature are describable as geometric tendencies. Space
and time are ineffable mysteries. We thus live in a state of wonder
when we take off the sunglasses that habitually shield us from
recognition of our ignorance. Yet, while man cannot basically
understand his world, he can act to alter that world. What are the
ultimate possibilities of such action?

The very thought of altering our own nature is alarming to us
because we fear the havoc we should raise if we presumed to
change the nature of life. History shows man taking over successive tasks thought earlier to be God's sphere of activity. Through
his rapidly increasingly ability to control greater amounts of motion of matter, man is becoming increasingly able to mix up the
universe, or order it according to his plans. With this increasing
ability he has not yet developed his capacity for love and brother-

hood, and his moral sensitivity to a degree that would insure his continuous development and survival. (One may assuredly say that all true progress is progress in the ability to love.) This gives man's material progress an uncertain aura, since it is evident that such progress may be regress when viewed in terms of the human values which it destroys. Yet, supposing human success in changing even the laws of the universe, would this not simply elevate God even higher in man's mind? Should we, then, have the courage to continue, trusting that, unlike Icarus, we shall realize when we are flying *too* high?

A new frontier is opening which allows us renewed hope. The new frontier is not merely space, but more profoundly the relationship of "inner space" to "outer space"—a bridge being built between mind and matter, beginning in our time and extending into the future. Specific electrical and chemical events affect the mind; we shall know how one day. In turn, the mind affects specific chemical and electrical events; how this is done we shall also know.

Goethe has said, *Wo Begriffe fehlen da stellt ein Wort rechten Zeit sich ein.* ("Where there is no understanding, there a word appears at the right time.") In the beginning was the Word and a new word may also be a beginning. A new word was created in 1960 to describe a new concept for man's venture into space: *Become* a spaceman; live in space as at home—if possible, better than at home! Do not take with you into space earth's hindrances and encumbrances. Be a free spirit in space, weightless and not weighted down by the limitations of terrestrial ancestry. Is such a man—the cyborg—possible?

The cyborg concept fits man for space without changing his heredity. For while it might be courageous to alter heredity to suit our wishes, it would also be foolhardy. We can reversibly change the cyborg beause he is a man-machine combination, but a man changed by heredity is a prisoner of this design for his lifetime.

The space traveler under the old concept took with him as much of earth's environment as possible—much as a fish would take water with him if he wanted to live on land. The cyborg concept, which in four years has become current in the English language, says: You wish to go into space? Then equip yourself with new forms of energy transformation so that you can live confortably and "naturally" in space. Fish, build yourself a lung! The material source of life is solar energy; it is abundant in space. We merely have to change our physiological use of this energy. Will this change our fundamental nature? Not much more than glasses or iron lungs change it.

The difference is merely that instead of using external or *attached* prosthetic devices, the man-made devices are now to be *incorporated* into the regulatory feedback chains—the homeostatic mechanisms that keep us viable for such an astonishingly long time.

The cyborg concept helps man overcome the limitations of his earthly birth and adapt himself to space by using the accumulated experience of mankind plus his own courage and inner drive. By such participant evolution he is also about to bring us a step nearer to understanding the relationship between inner and outer space (or mind and universe) as a necessary corollary to the evolution of physiologic means for the creation of cyborgs.

It is thus a measure of man's courage, his ability and his being that, faced with outer space, he should look inward for a guide to the direction in which he should go for the answers he seeks, and fly away from earth to become a new and, he hopes, better being.

Dr. Manfred Clynes

1 *The Cyborg—and Why*

What are some of the devices necessary for creating self-regulating man-machine systems? This self-regulation needs to function without the benefit of consciousness, in order to cooperate with the body's own autonomous homeostatic controls. For the artificially extended homeostatic control system functioning unconsciously, one of us (Manfred Clynes) has coined the term Cyborg.

"Cyborgs and Space," by Manfred Clynes and Nathan S. Kline, *Astronautics*, Sept. 1960, p. 27.

In an era so filled with wondrous and frightening things, the age of space for example, and the impending take-over by the computer and other machines, another development is taking place with little notice by the average person, unless he or she happens to *be* one of the new developments. In our midst, and growing steadily in numbers, is the latest evolutionary step in man, sometimes called by the odd name of "cyborg." Unheralded though it is, this hybrid human may well be a forerunner of the men of the future.

If we accept the theory of evolution at face value, man has reached his present position as master of the world through a gradual and natural process of change. Starting with a single-celled form of life somehow created out of the raw materials at hand, life has proliferated along many and various trails to where it now stands, with about 1 million species of animals and 267,000 of plants. Different men view evolution in different ways. Civilization is about 7,000 years old, but it was only about 2,500 years ago that Thales guessed at the phenomenon of evolution. And as recently as 100 years ago men still scoffed at the idea.

Julian Huxley, the eminent biologist in an eminent family of scientists and writers, sees not one evolution, but three. First there is evolution on the cosmic scale, the "stellar evolution" of the universe that set the stage for the second kind of evolution, that of biological evolution. Finally, there is social evolution, which stems from the actions and interactions of the individual products of biological evolution.

Nobel Prize winner P. B. Medawar further breaks biological evolution into four stages. In the first, life simply existed according to fixed and rigorous chemical and physical rules. An organism traveled through its life span like a weight falling to earth under the pull of gravity. There was no choice possible to the early living thing; its actions were completely instinctive.

Next came a second stage in evolution in which the organism possessed a brain that could receive stimuli from the external world and act on these "instructions."

Thus far Medawar's heredity is of a strictly genetic variety. But about half a billion years ago, give or take a million, a third stage manifested itself. Then, in addition to the genetic inheritance a living thing possessed, came something external— something we may call tradition. Animals pass on knowledge to their young: how and what to hunt, how to build nests, and so on.

This third stage of evolution became so well developed in man that some two hundred years ago it gave rise to a fourth stage of evolution: a systematic and rapid change in the nature of these traditions or instructions passed on from generation to generation of man in addition to the genetic inheritance, which changed not noticeably if at all in so short a time.

Medawar adopts the terms "endosomatic," or within the body, for genetic heredity, and "exosomatic" for that outside the body. The latter has changed man greatly despite the fact that endosomatically he is little different from an ancestor who lived many thousands of years ago. Exosomatic heredity, then, is an overriding factor that produces a different kind of man than would result with only genetic heredity working upon him.

Man has evolved genetically from lesser life forms. What will be the result of the new evolution? Julian Huxley suggested the term "transhuman" for a superior being aware of his potential and able to work toward it because of his knowledge. Nietzsche spoke of the "superman" toward whom man was only a rope across an abyss.

Benjamin Franklin called man a "toolmaking animal." Some modern writers disagree, suggesting that it was the tool that did the making, from animal into man, and that the tool is inexorably destined to supersede man and become superman. Some suggest that the next big step in evolution will see man himself extinct as the dodo, driven from the face of the earth by the very machines he built and which will some day outthink him.

The idea of artificial man, the synthetic human, is no new scare; it dates back to the Old Testament and earlier, and is simply resurrected and sharpened in focus by recent developments in electronics and other scientific fields. At present it is difficult to tell who is winning the war, although some battles seem to lean toward the machine. Hegel's dialectic may apply: thesis and antithesis result in a synthesis. Man, or machine? Perhaps "man-machine" will be the logical product, a compromise in which everybody profits. If man cannot beat the artificial creations that some see threatening his very existence, it might behoove him to join them. This is the basis for the cyborg idea.

Evolution, the old-fashioned *endosomatic* kind, has produced some amazing results. In Japan there are crabs of the Heike species that bear on their backs an awesome replica of the face of an Oriental warlord! How did such a strange thing come to be if not by some kind of weird magic worked by the crabs themselves or their protector? Biologist Huxley explains the face of man on the crab, which thus gains protection from being eaten, in this way: Long ages ago, chance dictated that a crab or two would be produced with a design roughly approximating an Oriental face on its back. Superstitious fishermen tossed these frightening caricatures back into the sea where they lived to produce more of their kind—complete with picture. Over the years, an artwork improved by punishment and reward has resulted in the startling picture the Heike crab presents today.

Except to the crab, this may be considered a superficial example of evolution. So too might be the evolution of birds' eggs that roll in a circle and thus are less likely to fall from a cliff ledge. The progess of the lungfish—from gut to swim bladder to lung—is a more dramatic evidence of evolution at work.

Nature can produce a result, given enough time. And nature has all the time it wants. But a living thing can take matters in its own hands—or feet or claws, or whatever—for its short-term and individual benefit. Crocodiles have been found with a considerable weight of stones in their stomachs, posing the puzzle as to what the stones are doing there. The answer seems to be that the stones are simply ballast to permit the amphibians to cruise lower in the water and thus not be as vulnerable as without such ballast! Such animal brilliance is a bit humbling, but man is the animal who wears shoes of alligator skin and carries luggage made of the same stuff, ballast or no. Man also possesses this ability to change himself, in spades.

Names are handy tags for thing and for beings. The term "automation" itself has done much to further the science of doing things automatically with machines. The name "bionics" added glamour and a catchword to an already fertile marriage of the sciences of biology and engineering. And so the word "cyborg" seems to have the ring needed to dramatize the latest evolutionary aspect of man. It is a coinage of Dr. Manfred Clynes, a research scientist engaged in basic research on brain function and the design of physiological instrumentation and apparatus, electronic data-processing systems, and ultrasonic devices.

As defined by Dr. Clynes, a cyborg—an abbreviation for "cybernetic organism"—is an "exogenously extended organizational complex functioning as an integrated homeostatic system unconsciously." More simply, a cyborg is the joining of a living thing with a nonliving device or devices. A moment's thought will bring to mind many such couplings, and the term can be interpreted broadly enough to include the homeliest man-machine combinations or in a narrower sense to mean only quite complex systems.

A man with a wooden leg is a cyborg. So is a man in an iron lung. More loosely, a steam-shovel operator or an airplane pilot is a cyborg. As I type this page I am a cybernetic organism, just as you are when you take pen in hand to sign a check. Reduced to this simplicity the concept loses much of its impact. By these lights, the caveman with his stone ax was the granddaddy of present-day more complicated cyborgs. If addition of a stone ax or pen to a man were all the word cyborg implied, there would be no reason for a book about it, and hardly an excuse for a name. But the cyborg goes far beyond the simple examples mentioned.

For wooden leg substitute an artificial limb of plastic and metal, powered with electronic muscles and controlled by the wearer's own nerve signals amplified by miniature transistorized equipment. For iron lung substitute implanted artificial heart or other internal organ that takes the place of a natural one. For steam-shovel operator substitute military technician who operates weapons of war remotely simply by "thinking about them."

Consider a cyborg spaceman whose body is artificially cooled far below the normal 98.6 degrees to prolong life and permit him to exist on a bare fraction of the "fuel" natural man would require. His body structure has been altered so that weightlessness does not harm him, and he is drugged or hypnotized to provide him with an artificial sense of gravity. Fed intravenously, he produces no waste products. His cells are immune to radiation normally dangerous to man. Electronically amplified limbs permit him to move as required even during the extreme stresses of blastoff and reentry, or other high-acceleration maneuvers.

Finally, consider another kind of cyborg, one altered artificially at, or even before, conception so that he grows into whatever physical form is required or desirable. An artificially produced human being with a body superior to natural man; with none of the weaknesses or susceptibilities to disease, and with whatever causes aging in human beings eliminated or at least drastically slowed down so that the cyborg will live not just a better, healthier life, but a much longer one as well.

A favorite question of philosophers, scientists and science fiction writers has long been whether or not man is simply part of nature. Involved in such a question are the other pertinent ones of semantics, cosmology, physics, metaphysics, ethics, morality, religion, et cetera. It would seem that man was indeed part of nature until his very recent past. He was surely a product of nature until he achieved the remarkable ability to contemplate his navel, himself, and his place in the scheme of things. From contemplation he moved quickly to dissatisfaction and a desire for change. We honor the thesis that necessity is the mother of invention. It is becoming necessary that man change his condition. At least he considers it desirable, and for some time he has not docilely accepted his environment, but altered it with a vengeance and himself along with it.

When man began to participate in the process of evolution, he moved out of nature, according to some thinkers on the subject. Man became a kind of *deus ex natura* and the result of his tamperings was not natural man but a bastardized form fathered in part by artificial agents. This view, however, depends on just how we define nature. After all, nature may be taken to imply all that is within our universe, not simply light and air, wind and water. Iron is part of nature, and so are the modern plastics man has made for his use. The laws of thermodynamics and the conservation of energy still hold. Nothing is gained or lost even though man juggles things about to suit his needs, desires, or capricious whims.

The atom bomb may be thus construed as part of nature, for if it is not, then what can it be? If we understand nature to mean not just natural forces and living things, but anything that can occur—or be made to occur—then man is still seen to be product and part of nature although he is 10 percent or even 90 percent plastic and metal. Even if pessimists prove to be correct and a creature that is 100 percent artificial holds sway, it may not be unfair to say that this too is natural evolution, no matter how unfortunate we may consider such an eventuality from where we sit.

For our purposes here, then, we shall consider man very definitely a part of nature, and his hastened, exosomatic evolution still a natural result of the given conditions and materials he arose from and now finds at his disposal. For better or for worse we are committed to what Clynes and Kline have termed "participant evolution." Man himself is now an important factor in his own development.

Homo sapiens is the one of all God's creatures most given to thinking, and the more he thinks the less happy he is with himself and his capabilities. Man differs from other animals in his ability to change things, and he lost no time in putting this ability to work. Not only has he changed his environment, but he has also gotten to work on himself.

With paint and powder and a variety of other cosmetics man has beautified himself and his female partner. These modest changes in natural man may be smilingly dismissed as mortal vanity, although more correctly they are genetic in nature. Paint and powder, padding, artificial hair and other items serve the primary purpose of attracting and impressing the other sex and thus insuring propagation of the race.

Man has also built mechanical aids, from the shovel upward in complexity, to make physical tasks easier. He has built computing machines that may be loosely connected to his own think-box to augment his natural reasoning ability. These developments may stem from laziness or from a natural drive toward progress. But to attribute all cyborgian developments to vanity, the sex urge, or laziness is not nearly the complete picture.

Vanity is responsible for elevator shoes, some dental work,

and self-mutilation ranging from lip stretching to nose jobs. But it is not vanity alone that makes a man want an artificial leg or arm. One of man's needs is to go on living to the fullest, even though handicapped. For these it is a case of "extraordinary people seeking out ordinary destinies" through the aid of such artificial devices. In addition to prosthetic limbs humans also often need artificial eyes and ears.

Because there is a reverse drive against propagation of the race in which basic instincts are overridden by social and economic pressures, some men and women fit themselves with artificial devices that make them a sterile type, which cannot (hopefully) reproduce itself. Other men and women seek out artificial help to *make* them become fruitful.

Man inherited war from nature, if we are to believe one camp, although another argues that there is nothing inherent to make us belligerent. Be that as it may, wars and rumors of them have long been with us and sadly threaten to continue. Such catastrophes leave in their wake the maimed and broken who require artificial aid if they are again to take a place in normal, or somewhere near normal, life. We may console ourselves that much of the work toward better artificial limbs and other parts is a direct outgrowth of work with war victims.

We should not lose sight of the fact that it is not war that makes most of the cripples or otherwise incapacitated. American automobile drivers are a prime example of man's inhumanity to man even off the battlefield and many more broken bodies must be rebuilt because of highway and other accidents.

Nature's slipups too must be repaired. Some babies are abnormal in one way or another and these defectives must be corrected in some fashion to be accepted members of society. A certain minimum of physical conformity seems necessary. Miracles are being wrought by doctors and technicians who create hips for youngsters born with none, and give fingers or arms or legs to the handicapped. Plastic surgery, seemingly a minor artificiality, is of tremendous importance to the person needing it. The body's inner parts too, its organs and plumbing, are overhauled and even replaced.

Genetically we adapt to changing environment through the Darwinian process of natural selection. That is, those of us best fitted to conditions survive, and breed progeny who, statistically, will also be best fitted. Darwin's findings ousted the older theory of acquired characteristics advanced by Lamarck, but now we see that our exosomatic evolution is something like Lamarckian evolution even more speeded up.

The hazards of traffic are part of our new environment. How long it would take nature to evolve humans with built-in safety helmets, seat belts, and neck braces is problematical. Man himself has to do this job of evolution, either before the fact by giving motorists eyes in the backs of their heads, better night lights and so on, or after the crash by putting them back together with metal and plastic and other substitutes.

Traffic, among the most overt environmental menaces, is by no means the only serious threat to existence. Of late we have hints that our penchant for puffing on burning tobacco can lead to serious consequences. Man, with characteristic perversity, is working on a solution: not eliminating the cause of trouble, but compensating for it. This we do with drugs, with operations and so on.

The nuclear age brought with it another threat: that of radiation damage that is not limited to wartime. Since we seem unable to eliminate activities of the atom, we are working on means to protect the living cell from the effects of its radiation.

Such worries, and the more trivial ones attendant on our daily breadwinning, status seeking, and child raising, all raise havoc with a physical constitution still geared to a "natural" environment in which all we would do is search for food, sleep, and produce young. Hearts and stomachs are big sufferers here, and so we are tinkering with these organs to keep ourselves alive, and meanwhile dosing ourselves with drugs not in nature's normal pharmacopoeia.

Along with a nuclear age we have an age of space, and again an extreme change in environment. Conditions out there are hostile, to say the least. There is no oxygen for breathing in outer space. There *is* plenty of dangerous radiation, however, including awesome solar flares that may make the Van Allen belt seem a sunbath by comparison. In direct sunlight an astronaut is cooked, and in darkness he freezes quickly. At least a nuisance is the fact that no food is available in space, or water either. There is no gravity, giving rise to the phenomenon of weightlessness. While this condition is perhaps not as dangerous as wild rumors of astronauts coming back to earth with bones softened to the consistency of sash putty would indicate, some physiological changes do undoubtedly take place. Even the psychological changes accompanying weightlessness are sufficient to send engineers to their thinking rooms for solutions to problems of sensory deprivation.

A trip to the moon will be of relatively short duration. The planets in the solar system will require journeys of years. To venture farther presumes living longer than man's accustomed three score and ten. How does this affect the configuration and structure of our astronaut? He may have to be a horse of another color than his earth-bound counterpart.

There are those scientists who suggest creation of cyborgs from scratch, tailored to the specific planet they voyage to. This would involve tinkering with the genes in the tiny egg cell and the much tinier sperm that fertilizes it. A second approach is to surgically alter an earth-being to accommodate him to the terrific gravity he will encounter, the gases he must breathe and so on. A third and more acceptable solution is the use of an earthman "amplified" electronically where necessary, doctored with drugs, deep-frozen, and properly shielded to keep out harmful radiation.

While we are dealing in space travel we should not forget the region of "inner space" beneath the sea. Here too is a hostile environment to which man must adapt. This will be a reverse process to that which brought living things from the sea in the first place and onto dry land. We cannot wait the hundreds of thousands of years that nature would require to refit us with gills and some means of standing great pressure at the depths. Instead we will do the job exosomatically, evolving technologically. We have already trained some of our number to breathe gases other than air to adapt to undersea life. A more drastic approach is that of learning to breathe *water*. Sounding like science fiction, this has already been accomplished with rats and dogs, and is suggested for humans.

Primitive cyborgs have been with us for centuries. Of late, however, the cyborg has become a sophisticate whose future is interesting to speculate upon. We have seen how the need first arose for the semiartificial man: replacements for amputated limbs, for damaged eyes or ears, and so on. Lesser "cosmetic" changes are effected for vanity's sake. Now consider an extension of both ideas. Those who feel the need for bustles and falsies, false eyelashes and colored contact lenses, wigs and teeth, might be candidates for similarly improved artificial replacements of warm-to-the-touch, resilient plastic. Where early spectacles and ear trumpets attempted to restore a part of normal perception, how about such devices that make vision and hearing better than what nature gave us in the first place? Hearing aids *are* being sold to people whose ears function perfectly but who want to hear even better. Telescopes and microscopes are ancient aids to human vision, but might not the person with normal vision appreciate contact lenses that give *better* than normal sight, with an attachment to permit night vision by means of infrared waves?

Science fiction envisions a world of amputees with artificial limbs made of a special lightweight metal and powered by atomic energy. These limbs are controlled by the wearer's own nerve impulses and capable of much more precise movement than normal human limbs and with many times their power.

The notion of replacing human brains is as old as science fiction, and wild rumors assert that wealthy men have bought the brains and other parts of younger men to replace their own deteriorative organs. An alternative that comes to mind is the electronic brain, as the computer has come to be called. Today men work closely with computers, engaging in conversation with the brighter ones. What remains is the further miniaturization of such machines and their incorporation first as a helmet, and later as an "implant." Or, better yet, some doctoring of our own ten-billion-cell brains that will make them more efficient for certain tasks that now give us all kinds of trouble.

The compatibility of electronic equipment with the human body was discovered not long ago. Electroencephalography is commonplace. Electronic cardiac pacemakers are becoming so. Scientists have succeeded in implanting a miniature radio transmitter in a rat, powering it with electricity from the animal's own body. From these preliminaries to the human cyborg with an implanted transmitter-receiver, capable of what amounts to mental telepathy, is how big a step? Or perhaps a slave cyborg, fitted only with the receiver and receiving his instructions and his very conscience from Big Brother at headquarters via radio?

William Barrett's recent novel, *The Fools of Time*, is based on the idea of a doctor's discovering the secret of eternal life. Here is man's age-old dream, and such a twentieth century version of the Fountain of Youth would usher in a wild stampede of those who wanted to live forever. No such elixir has been announced in the real world, but science is seriously studying the problem of aging and whether or not it is an inescapable aspect of life. Here would be the ultimate cyborg, a man-made man with immortal life.

Two approaches are suggested for such a being. In one an artificial body and organs would replace most of the "living" human, with only the original brain remaining. Another method would be alteration of the cells themselves, putting to work newly discovered secrets of the key to life believed locked in the giant molecule of DNA, the gene. It is one thing to talk glibly of such an eventuality, and something else again to effect it. However, the fact that man can think of such a goal, and the assurance that for some it is desirable, is an indication that it is within the realm of possibility.

In the following chapters of this book we will trace the cyborg from its humble beginnings many thousands of years ago, through its flowering in modern times, to a glimpse of what it may well become in the near future when cyborgs are extraordinary people —seeking extraordinary destinies.

2 Evolution to the Cyborg

In the alteration of himself man has a great deal further to go than in the alteration of his inorganic environment. He has been doing the latter more or less unconsciously and empirically for several thousand years, ever since he ceased being parasitic on his environment like any other animal, and consciously and intelligently for at least hundreds of years; whereas he has not been able to change himself at all and has had only fifty years or so to begin to understand how he works. Of course, this is not strictly true: man has altered himself in the evolutionary process, he has lost a good deal of hair, his wisdom teeth are failing to pierce, and his nasal passages are becoming more and more degenerate. But the processes of natural evolution are so much slower than the development of man's control over environment that we might, in such a developing world, still consider man's body as constant and unchanging. If it is not to be so then man himself must actively interfere in his own making and interfere in a highly unnatural manner.

J. D. Bernal
The World, the Flesh and the Devil
Dutton, 1929.

Retracing the evolutionary path that has led man from his early "natural" days to the present era of cyborgian revolution takes us far back in history. Anthropologists are in general agreement that because man's hands did not specialize into hooves, claws, or something else but rather remained as five flexible digits, he was thus separated from other animals soon after he learned to walk upright. He became the "toolmaking animal," thus creating a new species of man (or being created by his tools, if we accept one theory). At the same time, he instigated a new kind of evolution that worked from without his body at an accelerating rate while genetic heredity continued at the same cautious pace. Man could use his tools on himself.

Among the lower animals monkeys have been found to evidence toolmaking ability in joining two sticks to reach a bit of food placed out of reach. However, the monkey does not think to prepare a tool for some future need, whereas man learned foresight early. To cut down trees and carry on its way of life, the beaver had to develop sharp and powerful teeth. It had to *specialize*, and this came about through the evolutionary process of natural selection in which the fittest were more apt to survive, and their offspring likely to have the same characteristics. Man, not possessing natural teeth capable of cutting down a tree, substituted a tool of sharp rock. More than a million years ago, prehistoric men were using crude tools of rock and wood. This homely beginning was a first step toward the cyborg, crude though that beginning appears in comparison.

In like fashion, other sharp bits of stone served as knives and daggers. Finally, spears and then bows and arrows tipped with stone flakes made their appearance. When man mastered metal he substituted it for the stone, bone, and wood used previously. In making the tools, his technological ability was greatly increased. More important was the fact that the primitive agriculturist with a hoe of stone and wood was a *different* human from the one without such artificial extension of arms and hands. A warrior armed with a sword of metal was different from an unarmed man, as the latter was quick to appreciate when the two engaged in combat. A turtle is endowed with a shell by nature; man conceived and built a similar shield of hides and later of metal. He protected his head with an artificial covering, and did the same for other parts of his body, succeeding in a relatively short period of time in comparison with the naturally armored armadillo, who had to wait for genetics to fit him for his environment.

It was prophetic that man's early cyborg ventures taught him that with an artificial device he could *extend* his capabilities and achieve powers he did not possess naturally. The notion of using a substitute for some lost or useless natural part came much later in man's exosomatic evolutionary development. The skeletal remains of an amputee who lived out his life forty-five thousand years ago have been found in Iraq. But it was apparently only some five thousand years ago that man began to patch up his body's bones and flesh with artificial substitutes.

Artificial Substitutes

More advanced and specialized than worms and salamanders, in developing further men had lost their powers of regeneration. Life was hazardous, and limbs were lost or crippled by war, wild animals or disease. Ironically, the picture has changed today mainly in the substitution of automobiles and other machines for wild animals. At any rate, the idea came naturally to replace a missing leg with a stick or crutch. Early positive evidence of such a device is carved on the tomb of Hinkouf in Egypt. Depicting a man using a crutch, it dates back to 2830 B.C. The use of splints to support broken bones was common about this time in Egypt also. A fourth century Italian carving depicts a man with a useless right leg—thought to be wasted by anterior polio, incidentally—hopping gaily about on a wooden limb.

The urge to make man something more than he naturally was prevailed and attempts were made to couple man's limbs with the wings and tail feathers of a bird. Even with the cautionary tale of Icarus and Daedalus, pioneer scientist Leonardo da Vinci dared to design flapping wings to be strapped to a man's arms. He also invented the Mae West, by the way, a bladder attached to the chest and filled with air by blowing through a tube so that man might float more like a marine animal.

By 1500 a variety of orthopedic devices were in use, and men managed lives something near normal with leather and metal braces on damaged spines and necks, and special footwear designed to correct club feet. James Knight pioneered this important field in the United States during the 1800's.

More challenging was the problem of rebuilding handicapped men with mechanical contrivances to take the place of missing limbs. World War I created many victims on which to try out new ideas, and one of the techniques developed by German surgeons in military hospitals was "cineplasty." The wood and metal limbs of amputees were connected to a steel pin which in turn was actuated by the muscle in the patient's stump. Some earlier prosthetics had been simply cosmetic, or for looks. Those that did work operated by straps across the shoulders, with laboriously acquired skill on the part of the wearer in shifting his shoulders. With cineplasty the proper muscle itself was put to work, actuating the metal pin as it contracted under control of the wearer's brain.

Another development of the war was the Krukenberg "stump," the result of a rather monstrous operation that split the forearm of the amputee into two separate parts, a bone in each, which could open and close like a lobster's claw. All things are relative, however, and to the patient who previously had nothing but a useless stump, the Krukenberg offered at least limited grasping capability and was thus an improvement.

Not just limbs were lost or damaged in man's battle with man and nature. Eyesight and hearing were impaired, and teeth fell out or were sometimes knocked out. Toolmaking man learned that he could build eyeglasses that would greatly improve vision —the telescope gave man eyesight far better than nature had provided him with, incidentally. Crude ear trumpets helped the deaf somewhat. And artificial teeth filled the gaps so that men and women might eat and look better.

Thus far all of man's substitutions were artificial, but the idea of using living material was bound to occur and be put to the test even in days when such practices were likely to be lumped with witchcraft or worse. Whether such attempts stemmed from genius or simply the inability to fashion artificial replacements is open to question. For example, the Ecuadorian Indians as early as 1500 reportedly transplanted living teeth instead of putting in false ones. By the 1700's dentists in Europe were doing similar transplants with some success. Artificial teeth supplanted this more difficult method, but the idea of using living rather than artificial material had been established and would spread from the oral cavity to other body sites.

An artificial eye is better than an empty socket, even though such a replacement is not so useful as an artificial tooth. However, in 1844 a surgeon named Kissan felt that it was not enough to install a glass marble in an eye patient. In a bold operation he transplanted a section of cornea from the eye of a pig to a human patient. Although the "graft" failed to "take" permanently, there was a brief period of improvement in vision.

Ten years later J. M. Nussbaum tried another approach in the repair of failing eyes. He removed a plug of damaged cornea and replaced it with a glass implant. The operation, unfortunately, was not a success and surgeons returned to Kissan's technique. By 1887 A. Von Hippel succeeded, and valid records show that a patient of his saw through a pig's eye for at least a year.

Internal Repairs

It was natural that pioneer body builders limit themselves to the outwardly visible parts of their patients. They used artificial materials only externally. Foreign matter was permanently implanted in the body only in cases of gunshot, and the results did not augur particularly well for the future of intentional implants of metal or other materials. A surgeon could splint a broken bone from the outside, or add a wooden leg or arm, but what of internal prostheses—the addition of artificial parts inside the body?

In 1759 the English surgeon Hallowell succeeded in repairing a damaged artery by inserting a metal pin and wrapping the wound with thread. Here was a surgical technique much like that of the tinker or plumber. Was the internal structure of man actually amenable to such repairs? Brave doctors began to investigate and by 1775 there was hot controversy raging as to which metals were compatible with the body's physical and chemical environment.

Iron wire was used in early repairs of broken bones. Then the great Joseph Lister successfully used silver wire, and in 1829 J. Levert made studies of various metals in the body and reported that platinum was best. Surgeons now were beginning to treat man's internal structure like the skeleton of a building rather than a sacrosanct "natural" creation not to be desecrated by artificial intrusion. In addition to fine wire used to bind up shattered bones, metal or ivory plates were added, attached with screws and nails. The surgeon had become a sort of carpenter or cabinetmaker who fitted human bones together with the aid of saw and hammer and chisel, plus drill and screwdriver.

Brass, aluminum, red copper, steel, and magnesium were used in addition to iron, silver, and platinum. Different materials worked well in different applications, much as in the industrial metal trade. For example, magnesium was absorbed by the body. Strong chemical reactions took place, and these reactions actually promoted formation of new bone! But there were precautions to be taken. One surgeon used steel screws to attach a magnesium plate to bone and was dismayed to find that the galvanic action set up between dissimilar metals resulted in the magnesium's completely disappearing before the fracture could repair itself.

The mysteries of the galvanic phenomenon that produced minute amounts of electricity led to such strange results as involuntary extension of hand and fingers in a patient whose arm was patched internally with an aluminum plate attached with brass screws!

Nickel-plated steel proved excellent for use within the body, producing no irritation. Titanium, the metal now being used in aircraft, was used experimentally. An alloy called vitallium (cobalt, chromium and molybdenum) proved excellent and is still used in many prostheses. Stainless steel of certain types also was found very satisfactory.

One surgeon experimented with coil springs—placing them inside the bones of a cat, and later trying metal bars similarly placed for support of a mending bone. Sherman showed the advantages of vanadium steel attached with "self-tapping" screws rather than the traditional wood-screw thread. As in other kinds of joinery, the correct drills for the material at hand were found to be of great importance. Special "bone drills" were designed: angled more sharply and with a different cutting edge for the softer material. The diameter of the drill proved of great importance too. A hole of exactly the right size was needed, just large enough so that the self-tapping screw could cut its way securely into bone without splitting it, but not so large that the screw would work loose later on.

Other methods were developed for fastening bone fragments together. One of these, invented by V. Putti, was a "band tightener" much like the strapping machines that now fasten boxes and crates with metal bands.

In 1882 Gluck successfully used ivory clamps internally and Robert Abbe in 1894 used glass tubes to carry body fluids. Later, Theodore Tuffier substituted silver, paraffin-coated "cannula" or artificial blood vessels. Man was trying to extend artificial devices, prostheses, beyond their initial use merely for wiring broken bones and to use them to replace veins and arteries. But blood was a more difficult substance to handle than bone.

Living Transplants

While development of artificial limbs proceeded, there was another and far more daring bit of patchwork going on: the transplants hinted at in work with eyes and teeth. Along with legs lopped off or lost to disease, there were other parts of the body amputated too. Among these casualties were a surprising number of noses, lost through a particular kind of syphilis and for other reasons. The result was a horrible disfiguration of the human face, for the nose does far more for its owner than merely smell.

Attempts were made by victims to fashion substitute noses of various substances, but usually the only thing they could do was conceal the disfigurement beneath a handkerchief. However, as long as 2,000 years ago, daring surgeons attempted to fashion new noses—not of any artificial substance, but of human flesh!

Medical writings ascribe such operations to the Roman, Celsus, in A.D. 100, to Branca in Sicily, to the Hindustani Coomas, or bricklayer caste, and more recently and authoritatively to the Italian surgeon Gasparo Tagliacozzi toward the end of the sixteenth century. Various techniques were used, including the cutting of a skin flap from the forehead and shaping it into a new nose, and using skin from the patient's arm. Skin from donors was also tried but the idea was abandoned when it was found that such grafts didn't "take" permanently—the same trouble encountered by transplanters of teeth. The reason for such failures was to persist in latter-day transplantation techniques—the rejection of foreign tissue in the so-called "immune reaction."

Despite Tagliacozzi's reputed success, he fell into disfavor both with the Catholic church and with some of his colleagues. Other surgeons claimed that the nose grafts had not really been successful. The church was opposed on the grounds that such tampering with nature was immoral. In the face of such dual opposition, most of the medical profession shied away from the creation of new noses. The feeling against "rhinoplasty" operations, as the nose job is technically known, ran so high after Tagliacozzi's death that his body was disinterred from church ground and reburied elsewhere.

In 1794 an article appeared in *Gentleman's Magazine*, published in England, describing an operation performed on an Indian named Cowasjee and five British soldiers to provide them with new noses. The men had been mutilated by bandits. So successful were the grafts that a British doctor who saw the surgery performed a similar operation on another soldier who had lost his nose though improper treatment of disease with mercury. With this resurgence, rhinoplasty was accepted by the medical profession. Wonderful as was the nose graft technique, the long-range implications were far more important. For example, by the late nineteenth century, the Viennese surgeon Theodor Billroth was performing miraculous transplant surgery on diseased gastrointestinal tracts, giving his name to two famous surgical techniques, Billroth I and Billroth II. He also replaced with living material larynxes destroyed by cancer.

Much as the tinker had learned how to join similar metals, the surgeon was learning how to fuse together bits of living matter taken from the same individual. But as the metal worker was faced with a tougher task in joining different metals, so the surgeon was baffled when he tried other kinds of grafts. A flap of skin from Mr. A's forehead could be shaped into a new nose that would adhere to Mr. A's face. But skin from Mr. A would not "take" on Mr. B.

As early as 1670 a researcher named Macren reported some success in grafting a piece of dog's bone into a man. Such a graft is called a "heterograft." Attempts with skin were not as successful and grafts of frog skin onto human patients by Petersen in 1885 failed. More success was had with "homografts" or transplants between species.

In 1743 Abraham Trembley had grafted hydras together. The hydra is only a freshwater polyp, but before 1900 Ross Harrison was successfully grafting limbs onto salamanders and Braus repeated this procedure with tadpoles. In 1924 the rudimentary heart of an embryo was grafted by P. Stoehr, Jr. into another embryo from which the heart had been removed. B. D. Morozov in 1927 grafted the heart of one *living* triton into another.

These transplants were performed on lower forms of life. Attempts on higher forms met with much less success, but continued experiments were made.

The Vital Organs

Thus far the business of replacing missing or ailing bits and pieces of the human body was confined for the most part to the grafting of skin and bone, surgical work on the gastrointestinal tract, and attempts at eye and tooth transplants. Of the organs, the stomach and sex glands had been the subject of some work, successfully in the case of the former, and not successfully in the latter. Tinkering with the heart and other vital organs was a more difficult proposition, particularly with the heart. Even the business of substituting artificial passageways for the blood had been found fraught with difficulty. But men could dream, and they did. And when they had dreamed sufficiently long, they tried gropingly to make dreams come true.

In 1628 Giovanni Colle made a statement to express the feelings of many and to inspire fiction writers and medical workers alike. "If a man in his old age had but the eye of an adolescent would he not see like the adolescent?" Colle asked. "Would he not feel and reason like a youth if he had the heart and brain of a youth? Likewise if he obtained the blood of a youth he would live like the youth."

Blood was life, obviously, and that vital fluid as well as the pump that circulated it were the object of much experiment even centuries ago. Colle's plea for the blood of a youth was anticipated as early as 1492, the year that Columbus discovered the New World. A new world in medicine was explored too when a "cross-transfusion" of the blood was performed on Pope Innocent VIII. Dr. Abraham Meyse connected the bloodstream of the ailing pontiff to those of three healthy boys, hoping that their systems would purify the Pope's bad blood. Unfortunately the daring scheme ended in disaster for all concerned, and Meyse fled the country for his own life.

After Harvey had correctly described the circulation of the blood, surgeons fared better in their attempts at transfusion and cross-circulation. Anastomosis, the joining of blood vessels, progressed to the point where it was a fairly common operation. By 1812 the French physician Le Gallois could say, "If one could substitute for the heart a kind of injection . . . of arterial blood, either natural or artificial . . . one would succeed easily in maintaining alive indefinitely any part of the body whatsoever."

The circulation of the body fluids was now being treated as an engineering problem, a problem in hydraulics and pumping and requiring some of the same devices and techniques. In 1828 Kay accomplished artificial circulation in a living system to restore the "irritability of dying muscles." By 1849, the days of the gold rush in America, Gustav Lobel successfully "perfused" a kidney with an artificial circulatory system, and in 1859 Edouard Brown-Sequard's technique made it possible to oxygenate blood, not with lungs, but a syringe inserted into an artery.

Ten years later Karl Ludwig and Oskar Schmidt improved the perfusion apparatus, and de Cyon used it to keep the heart of a frog beating artificially for forty-eight hours. He was later able to demonstrate with the same equipment how the liver functioned by maintaining it alive outside the body.

Thus far only a simple "pressure circulation" had been achieved in the laboratory, but von Fry and Gruber attained pulsating pressure that more nearly duplicated living circulatory systems. In 1912 workers using this new equipment removed the heart, lungs, and abdominal organs of animals and kept these organs alive artificially for periods of up to ten hours.

Sustaining life in organs removed from the body indicated that it might be possible to place these organs in another body and have them function. Alexis Carrel, writing in 1929, tells of Cristiani and his transplanting of thyroid tissue from a mother to her thyroid-deficient child. The child was cured. Later she married and became pregnant. The thyroid grafts reportedly not only remained alive, but grew as normal glands.

The Russian, S. Voronoff, conducted his notorious monkey gland experiments during the 1920's. Working first with monkeys in whom he transplanted the testes of other monkeys, Voronoff then tried the experiment on men. Initial rejuvenation was reported, but perhaps this was only wishful thinking on the part of the senior recipients. There was no lasting benefit from the transplants. What happened was that the transplanted testes slowly withered away, in some cases completely absorbed in the new host. Differentiation was the problem. Unlike simpler forms of life that were apparently built to the same blueprint, higher forms varied from one another even in the same species. The very protection that made human tissue immune to infection also made it reject "foreign" tissue in the form of a transplant.

In the first decade of the twentieth century Carrel was transplanting organs in dogs. Voronoff had tried a human kidney transplant in addition to his testes grafts, but this was not successful. The operation was successful in dogs, and lungs and livers were transplanted as well. Finally, Carrel succeeded with even the heart of a dog. A more radical transplant operation was that of Dr. Charles C. Guthrie, who attempted grafting a second head onto a dog. Such a freak, found sometimes in nature, was understandably considered by many a gruesome joke of the vivisectionist, better left to nature itself.

Carrel also conducted experiments in keeping alive tissue placed in a bath of nutrient material. Most famous of these was the "chicken-heart" which "lived" in the laboratory until it died for lack of attention during World War II, after some thirty years in its solution of food. During the 1930's Carrel's assistant was a young aviator named Charles Lindbergh, famous in his own right. For Carrel he developed a "perfusion pump" that circulated fluid to organs being kept alive outside the body.

Dr. Carrel had successfully met the three requirements of such perfusion of organs: those of mechanical, surgical and chemical needs. His conclusions were that cultured organs could be kept alive for indefinite periods; that their structure could be made to vary according to the composition of the fluid fed them by the perfusion equipment; and that some day it would be possible to treat diseased organs outside the body, much as mechanical parts were repaired "on the bench." Thus the stage was being set for another concept in the artificial man: that of artificial vital organs.

Colle's dream was beginning to be realized. He had mentioned substituting the eye of a youth, and some humans had at least seen through the eyes of a youthful pig. Youthful blood was indeed beginning to aid the ailing through the improving technique of transfusions. There was a glimmer of hope that organs might be transplanted successfully, although that amazing organ called the brain did not seem to lend itself to such an operation. However, man had for centuries operated on the brain surgically to change the mental characteristics of its possessor and crude "lobotomies" were suggested in the skeletal remains of even primitive peoples. There was another way of altering the mind: that of chemical change through drugs.

The cyborg's history, then, begins around 1,000,000 B.C. Tool-making man used artificial adjuncts first to extend his capabilities over those of the animal, which did not make tools. Then for a shorter period of time he coupled man and artificial device as a means of repairing the ravages of time and the other elements. By the early twentieth century this secondary evolution had resulted in semiartificial men of a fairly sophisticated nature, beings not found in nature but created partly by man himself.

All this, impressive as it was, was but a prelude to what was to come. The cyborg revolution trailed the industrial revolution by centuries but was finally touched off by new technologies that date from about the time of the Second World War. Practically every idea of altering man to create superman, and even immortal man had been conceived far earlier, awaiting only the means of implementation to move from concept to hardware. The fictional Dr. Frankenstein had stated the case well:

I prepared myself for a multitude of reverses; my operations might be incessantly baffled, and at last my work be imperfect; yet when I considered the improvement which every day takes place in science and mechanics, I was encouraged to hope my present attempts would at least lay the foundations for future success.

In recent times scientific progress has accelerated at a great rate and the improvement Frankenstein was confident of has come to pass. We move now to the cyborg boom, a contemporary phenomenon few of us are yet aware of.

3 *Cyborg Revolution*

Man seems to be entering one of the major crises of his career. His whole future, nay the possibility of his having any future at all, depends on the turn which events may take in the next half century. It is a commonplace that he is coming into possession of new and dangerous instruments for controlling his environment and his own nature. Perhaps it is less obvious that he is also groping toward a new view of his office in the scheme of things, and toward a new and racial purpose. Unfortunately he may possibly take too long to learn what it is that he really wants to do with himself. Before he can gain clear insight, he may lose himself in a vast desert of spiritual aridity, or even blunder into self-destruction. Nothing can save him but a new vision, and a consequent new order of sanity, or common sense.

> W. Olaf Stapledon
> *Last and First Man, A Story of the Near and Far Future*
> Jonathan Cape & Harrison Smith, 1931.

Genetic evolution, a process of mutation and natural selection, is a slow and steady thing. *Homo sapiens* A.D. 1965 hardly differs physiologically from his counterpart of A.D. 1865 or even 1865 B.C. To be sure, man today is taller, and in some cases females reach puberty earlier than did their ancestors. But these differences are not attributable to the genes; they result from the environment man has created for himself. Here is a key to the cyborg's inevitability.

Children born today would revert to the runtier specimens of yesterday if fed on food then available and exposed to primitive environmental conditions. We can expect no marked changes in man genetically for a long time, barring violent mutations, either natural or man-made.

36

Secondary evolution, the participant evolution that is the force behind the cyborg, is not proceeding at the crawling rate we assume for genetic evolution. True, secondary evolution was a late starter and slow runner for much of the distance to the present. The making of tools seems in retrospect a sudden breakthrough, but actually it too was a long and slow process so that even after thousands of years of operation it has produced few humans very different from the conventional product. In the last two decades, however, the picture has changed radically.

Visualize an upward sloping line on a graph, with man's ascent determined for any point in time along the base line by measuring the height of the slope. A primitive statistician predicting man's future condition might have extended the graph with a straight line. Then for any year ahead he could pick off man's position and thus determine his evolutionary progress. Genetically, that is. Secondary evolution is no straight-line process but a curve that has suddenly begun to climb almost vertically.

In the preceding chapter we saw a hint of this accelerated progress but it was only the vaguest hint of what was to come. Historians will note the decade of the 1940's as a key period in scientific and technological advance. It was as though man had slowly infiltrated unknown territory for hundreds of years and then suddenly claimed it for his own.

The new era has been called by many names. The Atomic Age, the Computer Revolution, the Era of Cybernetics. It was the Electronic Age, the Age of Automation, and significantly it was the Space Age. Less obviously, it was the Cyborg Revolution, or perhaps the Evolution Revolution as man's civilization created both the need for further changes in himself and the technological means with which to produce these changes.

The atomic bomb brought boon and bane. Man had a new weapon—for good and for evil. He had new materials, new power sources and new blast and radiation effects to protect against. With automation came the realization that man was being uprooted economically and socially. Increasing population threatened the planet with overcrowding. Pacing other fields, there was new medical knowledge: drugs that gave man calmness in the face of a maddening new culture, and also a weapon against overpopulation. The military, which had created primitive cyborgs in the swordsman, the armored knight and the frogman, saw the need and advantage of a more advanced artificial man. The push into space disclosed an environment far different from and more hostile than that on earth. The time was ripe for cyborg progress and that progress came, so rapidly that most of us are still unaware of what has already happened, and have only an inkling of what is going to happen: man has created a new environment; now he must fit himself into that environment.

There are three broad areas of development toward artificial man. First, artificial limbs, organs and other parts; second, the transplantation of living tissues and organs; and third, duplication and alteration of man's hereditary genetic structure. Startling progress has recently come in all three of these areas.

Cyborg "Hardware"

Today war does not cause the bulk of our amputees. There are far more civilian cases. The automobile accidents that kill 40,000 Americans annually maim another 500,000, year in and year out. One recent estimate gives 40,000 U.S. veteran amputees of all wars, and 500,000 civilians similarly handicapped. But war is more spectacular, it hits home harder. And because the military sometimes seem to have more conscience, more sense of duty than our civilian institutions, war spurs more development in the field of prosthetics than does peace. This was significantly true of World War II, and there are quadruple-amputee veterans wearing all artificial limbs and living useful lives. Instead of rigid "wooden legs," fully articulated limbs now permit the wearer to really walk. Along with the functional "hook" appear lifelike plastic hands capable of grasping.

Cineplasty has progressed to a fine art, but there are other types of power available as well for artificial arms and hands. Some prosthetics use electricity, some use hydraulic pressure, and some are charged with carbon dioxide gas. These benefit not only war casualties, but civilian amputees as well.

While new artificial limbs represented only improvements on an old idea, there was another development to greatly affect the inner man as well. Prosthetic devices had taken the place of bones and some other internal structure, and laboratory work with animals hinted at the possibility of replacement organs but until the 1940's about the only artificial internal organ in use was the "iron lung." Since it worked from outside the patient it was hardly an internal organ anyway. Real artificial internal organs were on the way, however.

In 1945, amidst the physical and mental distractions of war raging around him, the Dutch doctor Willem Kolff struggled mightily to complete a project he had been working on for years. Despite wartime restrictions and other pressures, Kolff succeeded with what materials he could scrape together in building the first workable artificial kidney.

It would seem that a man who built an artificial kidney in the midst of the havoc of war could do much more under better conditions. Kolff has indeed done so, and he has been joined by other workers in many countries in producing not only better artificial kidneys—including some that have been implanted *within* experimental animals—but better "heart-lung machines." These take over temporarily while the patient's organs are being operated on or are otherwise incapable of sustaining life. New materials, including plastics and metals, accelerated development of such "hardware." Electronics was also a potent factor.

Electronics dates back to Fleming's "valve," the pioneer vacuum tube on which the radio industry was built. But it was only recently that the electronic age really arrived. There are many reasons for this sudden flowering of a technology that had been available for half a century. The demands of the military in World War II led to development of sophisticated electronic equipment.

An example is radar, and another is the proximity fuse used to explode artillery shells in the area of the target.

Early electronic devices were still quite bulky, even though they were small in comparison with the equipment they superseded. To put a radio transmitter and receiver in the tip of an artillery shell obviously required the miniaturizing of such devices. Very small tubes were developed, and later the transistor and other semiconductor devices truly revolutionized electronics. Now it was possible to build tiny equipment, operating with very low power. And the stage was set for further exploitation of electronics in the field of medicine.

Developments in another field paralleled this miniaturization breakthrough. For a long time it had been known that the living body generated appreciable amounts of electricity. Studies of brain "waves" proved this organ generated electricity. Furthermore, meaning could be extracted from these electrical pulses. This discovery indicated that life and electronics were not completely foreign but readily and usefully compatible.

The spark of life, for example, turned out to be literally that. Electricity generated in muscle surrounding the heart energizes the beating of the organ that pumps five quarts of blood each minute through our bodies. And when man's own spark failed, an electronic "pacemaker" could take over and keep the heart beating.

Thus far we have been describing involuntarily produced electricity in living things. Such "shocks" can also be produced on demand, as in the electric eel, or when we want to move some part of our body. Our nerves conduct electrical signals from our brains to the muscles in question, in a fashion analogous to an electromechanical system. If we could learn to recognize these tiny electrical signals, and harness them, there are any number of interesting things we could do. For example, the Russians have apparently succeeded in operating an artificial limb with the wearer's own brain signals. The potential of this seemingly very unlikely application is evident in subjects trained to elicit responses far more specific and delicate than the body is normally capable of. Beyond this are such fanciful ideas as the remote operation of equipment, including driving a car without physically touching any of the controls.

The science of cybernetics, established in 1947 by Norbert Wiener, was a potent factor in showing the similarity and compatibility of living and artificial systems and rationalized the idea of applying engineering to living things.

After the introduction of cybernetics, an offshoot science was dignified with the name "bionics," a further realization by biologist and engineer that in many ways man could be equated with machine and vice versa. Stemming directly from cybernetics, bionics has the merit of a more apt and readily understood name. Somewhere between the "bloody" bionicist who probes the living system, and the engineering bionicist who studies those findings to build a better artificial system, is the worker whose field is the cyborg, a mating of man and machine.

Because of cybernetics and bionics, the brain, man's most wonderful organ of all, came under more intense scrutiny. Neurophysiologists have long sought the key to the brain's workings, and development of the electronic computer hinted a new approach for their research. Despite obvious differences, there were crucial and inescapable mental similarities between ENIAC's children and the children of Adam.

Progress in Transplants

While "artificial organists" developed their specialties, other scientists concerned with transplantation of *living* organs were making similar strides. An accident in a Yugoslav nuclear plant severely injured a number of workers, but with bone marrow transplants from human donors the men were saved. It was found that a milder form of the radiation that nearly killed them overcomes the "immune reaction" that causes rejection of such transplants. This technique has been used in many cases. There are other methods of overcoming the rejection, including drugs, hypothermia, and surgery.

Transplants of human kidneys from donors began to succeed. At first only between identical twins, then relatives, and finally between unrelated humans and even other animals. Liver transplants were successful. Even more remarkable, the heart of a monkey was transplanted in a human, and functioned for a short period of time.

Surgeons dared to tackle ever larger tasks of putting people back together. In the past, fingers had been stitched onto unfortunates who lost them in accidents. Ears had been reinstalled, as had noses. Now came success with whole arms and legs. Limbs completely severed accidentally were replaced and survived, even to nerve regeneration that permitted limited movement.

With the existence of techniques for overcoming the immune reaction, plus the new idea of "banks" of spare parts for humans in need of them, another concept was put into practice. If it is possible to graft an arm, could an arm from a donor be grafted instead? On a lesser scale the idea was tried. A South American sailor lost a hand in an accident, and it was replaced with a hand removed from a corpse. Unfortunately the graft did not take, and had to be removed soon after it was attached. But the dam had been broken.

Standing in the way of such operations were not only physical and technical problems but moral, religious, and sociological barriers as well. Understandably, surgeons preferred not to have a rash of wild-eyed publicity attendant on such operations, and often experimental surgeries were kept secret as long as possible both as an ethical procedure and to guard against a hue and cry from outraged moralists or religious zealots.

Not surprisingly, the idea of furnishing a human with the vital organs of a lesser animal is abhorrent to many. Yet when there is but one alternative and that is death, reluctance dwindles sufficiently to tolerate what had seemed an act against nature, God, or both.

While controversy still surrounds and impedes progress with transplants from one species to another, the idea of the bone bank, the eye bank, muscle bank, nerve bank, skin bank and so on rouses far less opposition than once was the case. With improved techniques in recent years, the number of corneal grafts, for example, has climbed to 10,000 a year. There is need for 30,000, and further expansion of the parts bank idea is necessary.

The most optimistic transplanter of human organs is not yet ready to discuss brain banks, from which those of us sick in the head might obtain a replacement. Even with lesser animals this organ switch has not been accomplished and only recently were monkeys' brains kept alive outside their bodies.

The Key to Life

While cyborg revolutionaries were making great progress with artificial replacements for body parts and also in transplanting living parts, another phase of the evolution of artificial man was booming too. In the laboratory, researchers were growing living tissue in a variety of forms from serums to human embryos. An Italian doctor fertilized an egg cell artificially and grew the resulting embryo for almost a month until abnormalities evidenced themselves. The Catholic church reacted strongly to what it considered immoral acts, and the work was halted.

Alarming as is the idea of growing life in a test tube, there are other developments that make it seem almost prosaic by comparison. Researchers at an American university recently were able to synthesize living muscle, using "raw" chemicals. One of the compounds used is called ATP, short for adenosinetriphosphate. Another scientific acronym, DNA (for deoxyribonucleic acid), makes the muscle builders' work seem only a prologue to the creation of life itself.

Nucleic acid was discovered by a German scientist shortly after Gregor Mendel read his paper formulating what would come to be known as genetics. In the 1940's other scientists established the fact that nucleic acid, or deoxyribonucleic acid, was actually the giant molecule of the gene itself. Not content with having identified the gene, intrepid researchers the world over immediately attempted to synthesize it from nonliving material. In a remarkably short time, they seem to have succeeded.

The worst—or best—thing that can be said about the resulting rash of wild headlines prophesying that man will shortly create life, and even tailor new forms of life, is that they are probably true. Even for those who scoff at talk of "genetic engineering," in which the genes are altered to produce supermen, there is the sobering awareness that the greater miracle has already been wrought. If life can be created artificially, then refinement of the product is but a detail that will be solved in time.

To the scientists who recently and timidly have suggested that, using the laboratory techniques pioneered by Carrel, we might one day "grow" replacement parts for humans, their predictions must already seem timid indeed alongside talk of growing an entire human from scratch and a batch of chemicals.

Paralleling the work with DNA is tremendous research effort into the phenomenon of aging, much of it backed by the federal government. Despite disclaimers by the more cautious, there are intriguing hints that the process of growing old can be halted or at least slowed, probably by tinkering with the gene.

DNA is a magical three-letter combination that may one day make all other work toward superman seem child's play but this does not cause a lessening of effort in other directions. Besides the technological areas already discussed are other exotic fields such as "cryogenic" or very-low-temperature research. Here is a potent tool for partisans of hypothermia as the cold road to immortality.

Until recently the cyborg concept, except for the simplest patchwork, has been mostly a dream in the minds of fiction writers and a few scientists and engineers. Quite suddenly the dream exploded into accomplished fact as knowledge and technology acquired in a variety of fields implemented ideas germinated centuries ago.

Specifics will be discussed in the chapters that follow. As we shall see, much has been done. Overnight the "self-made man" has become more than a figure of speech. For some, to be sure, this phenomenon is no more than damning proof of the horror of unskilled labor. For others it holds out the promise of not only life itself but better life. And that is quite a promise.

4 *The Human Machine*

Man has been given power over his environment by the shape of his skeleton. The limbs consist of articulate levers, composed of three segments. The upper limb is mounted upon a mobile plate, the shoulder blade, while the osseous girdle, the pelvis, to which the lower limb is jointed, is almost rigid and immobile. The motive muscles lie along these bones. Near the extremity of the arm, these muscles resolve into tendons, which move the fingers and the hand itself. The hand is a masterpiece. Simultaneously it feels and it acts. It acts as if endowed with sight. Owing to the unique properties of its skin, its tactile nerves, its muscles, and its bones, the hand is capable of manufacturing arms and tools. We never would have acquired mastery over matter without the aid of our fingers, those five small levers, each composed of three articulated segments which are mounted upon the metacarpus and the bones of the wrist. The hand adapts itself to the roughest work as well as to the most delicate. It has wielded with equal skill the flint knife of the primitive hunter, the blacksmith's hammer, the woodcutter's ax, the farmer's plow, the sword of the medieval knight, the controls of the modern aviator, the artist's brush, the journalist's pen, the threads of the silk-weaver. It is able to kill and to bless, to steal and to give, to sow grain on the surface of the fields, and to throw grenades in the trenches. The elasticity, strength and adaptiveness of the lower limbs, whose pendulum-like oscillations determine walking and running have never been equaled by our machines, which only make use of the principle of the wheel. The three levers, articulated on the pelvis, adapt themselves with marvelous suppleness to all postures, efforts, and movements. They carry us on the polished floor of a ballroom, and in the chaos of the ice-fields, upon the sidewalks of Park Avenue and on the slopes of the Rocky Mountains. They enable us to walk, to run, to fall, to climb, to swim, to wander all over the earth under all conditions.

Dr. Alexis Carrel
Man the Unknown
Harper, 1935.

To call our body a machine is to stretch the imagination not at all; it is that in every sense of the word. It is a purposeful structure, made up of a power supply, control system, pumps and plumbing, mechanical devices, electrochemical circuits, and so on.

Granted that the human body is a machine, the fact remains that there are machines and there are machines. As Dr. Carrel points out:

> Indeed, both a machine and our body are organisms. But the organization of our body is not similar to that of the machine. A machine is composed of many parts, originally separate. Once these parts are put together, its manifoldness becomes unity. Like the human individual, it is assembled for a specific purpose. Like him, it is both simple and complex. But it is primarily complex and secondarily simple. On the contrary, man is primarily simple and secondarily complex. He originates from a single cell.

The human structure is of such marvelous complexity, intricacy and efficiency that man is not expected to equal it with any machine of his own making. Nature has been at the job for more than a million years, and has built billions of test models. The human machine has stood the road tests of time; through competition in a tough marketplace it has been constantly improved. Useless changes have been weeded out and only the improvements have been retained. No expense has been spared to make man ideally suited for his environment—the "natural" environment he lived in until quite recently.

From the viewpoint of the engineer, man is an automaton, capable of locomotion, manual labor, communication, and control. Man requires fuel to provide energy, air to supplement that fuel, and a supply of water for various functions including the removal of wastes. He has a "duty cycle" of 16 hours on to 8 hours off.

Basically the human machine comprises a framework, extremities for locomotion and the handling of objects, internal components including pumps, valves, chemical plants and filters, a mechanism for reproducing itself, and a control box atop the whole business to receive and transmit information and to operate the machine. The entire assembly is covered with suitable material.

Very briefly let us look at these various parts of the whole and compare them with man's admittedly cruder but similar artificial mechanisms that in some cases have been substituted for parts of the human machine.

Skeleton

As the engineer would, let us start with the frame of the human machine, or its skeleton, to use the more familiar term. The human skeleton is made up of more than 200 bones and accounts for almost one-fifth the body's total weight. The key bone—or collection of bones—is the backbone. From 32 to 34 vertebrae, joined in a more or less graceful double curve something like the classic archer's bow, make up the backbone. With such a curved spine it is difficult to imagine how the soldier achieves the ramrod effect traditional to his calling.

Because man has stood erect only relatively recently, slow changes are still taking place in his backbone. At present it is an occasional source of trouble when disc slippage occurs between individual vertebrae. Meantime, man himself corrects this spinal shortcoming with various surgical techniques or by external bracing.

Atop the backbone is the skull, actually a collection of twenty-three bones. Eight of these form the cranium, protecting the brain, eyes, and ears. In the infant they are separate to permit any needed distortions of the head during the process of birth, but in later life the bones fuse together to make a single sturdy shell.

The brain is the only organ completely sealed in bone. However, the other organs need some protection too, and attached to the backbone are a dozen pairs of ribs (occasionally thirteen) that arch around the lungs and the heart. The upper ten pairs of ribs come together in the breastbone; the eleventh and twelfth do not so meet in the middle and are often referred to as "floating ribs."

Beneath the skull and neck are bones that form an anchoring place for the arms. The shoulder blades are large, spade-shaped bones that provide a large reinforcing "gusset," to use the terminology of the engineer. A socket is provided at the outer end of each shoulder blade. Above and in front of the shoulder blades are the "collar bones" that bridge from shoulder blades to breast-plate. Attached to the socket of the shoulder blade is the upper bone of the arm, the humerus. It in turn terminates in another socket to which are attached two bones that make up the fore-arm: the radius and ulna. Like ball and socket joints of a mechanical nature, those of the arms permit movement in a hemisphere from each shoulder; with the extra articulation of the elbow and wrist, the hand is able to reach just about anywhere except the spot on our back that itches the worst.

Division of the arm bone into two in the lower arm permits the rotation or "pronation" of arm and hand, a very useful maneuver we scarcely appreciate until the arm is in a cast. At the wrist the two bones rejoin in another socket from which the bones of the hand radiate. Fingers and thumbs are jointed, and the resultant ability of "prehension," or grasping—principally with thumb and first two fingers—is important in setting man apart from some of the lower species. This is the toolmaker ability.

At the lower end of the backbone is the pelvis, a bony structure something like two shoulder blades joined in the middle. The pelvis, actually another collection of many bones, is joined to the backbone at the center and forms a ring, or pelvic girdle. This ring forms the birth canal, and here again nature is still evolving its human product. Even though the opening in the pelvis is larger in women than men, there is still occasional trouble at birth, especially as infants' heads get larger. Given time, nature will provide an even larger pelvic girdle through which the new-born can enter the world with greater comfort for all concerned.

At the bottom of the pelvis are sockets for the leg bones,

similar to but larger than those in the shoulder blades. Into these fit the ball of the femur, or thigh bone. This is a single bone, the longest in the human skeleton. From here on down to the ground we have a sturdier repeat of the arm's bone structure. Below the knee are two bones, the fibula and tibia, terminating in the ankle bone to which are attached the foot bones.

The legs and feet differ from the arms and hands, of course. Protecting the knee joint is a loose piece of bone called the knee-cap. We often wish we had similar insulation for our elbows when we bump them painfully. In the foot, the heel is far more pronounced than the heel of the hand. In the vanished past, man's ancestors walked on all fours as babies do today. Rising to two feet, they found balance awkward, and slowly the heel was thrust more prominently backward to provide simulation of an extra point of contact. Between the ball of the foot and the heel the bones have formed an arch for strength and perhaps to preserve the effect of the two points of contact. The process is not yet quite complete, and fallen arches and resultant flat feet plague some of us.

The little toe has become of less and less importance, now being mainly a source of bunions and corns. The big toe, once opposable like the thumb, has lost this ability since it is not needed, though it is instructive to watch an infant playing with its feet and occasionally grasping with big toe and others in something like the prehension of the hand.

This is the basic, bony framework of the human machine, the girders or chassis to which are attached the various components that put it into motion. Our bones are structural shapes; one anthropologist has called four-legged animals "bridges that walk" for their similarity to the principles of cantilevering used in bridge-building. Bones are levers, protective shells or cages, and ball and socket joints. They are designed individually, and as complexes, to provide strength and flexible movement. The engineer can roughly duplicate man's frame, but has not yet learned to build such structural shapes that grow and also have the ability to heal themselves.

Besides bone there are two similar materials used importantly in the body. In our skull are thirty-two teeth, unless we have met with an accident, including that of old age. Used for cutting and grinding, the teeth are obviously of very hard, and yet strong material. They are not bone, which is far softer, but calcium phosphate. The first mammals were equipped with sixty-six teeth. Man is down to less than half that number, and anthropologists suggest that an even further reduction is in view in the years of genetic evolution ahead. Wisdom teeth that fail to penetrate are an example. Perhaps a million years hence we will have only twenty teeth.

Teeth are harder than bone; cartilage is softer. It is, in fact, bone that didn't quite make it. A baby is born with much of his backbone still cartilaginous, with hardening proceeding during the early years. Adults retain some cartilage, however. In places we need more support than mere skin, yet more flexibility than bone can give. The nose is an example: boxing would be even more hazardous with a bone clear to its tip.

There is also cartilage in the ears, fortunately, else they would droop like those of the elephant. Part of the rib cage too is cartilage, and this intermediate material is found in several other places in the body.

Muscles

Marvelous though the skeleton is, it is a static structure. Although youngsters, and some oldsters, cannot convince themselves of this, the bony remains of a human cannot get about alone, any more than a drawbridge can lift its span without motive power. The muscles provide this power. As an indication of how important a part of the machine they are, they account for about 40 percent of the weight in man. Women have about one-fourth less muscle than men, and must rule their mates by other than physical strength.

Most obvious uses of the muscles are moving our arms and legs, and manipulating our jaws so that we can talk or chew up our food. But other muscles pump blood through the heart at 2½ gallons a minute, and air into the lungs at the rate of 5 gallons in the same amount of time. These muscles operate without our conscious control; in fact we find it most difficult to stop them from operating. Even the infant who holds his breath until he turns blue ends by gasping for air involuntarily before he can lose consciousness.

Other muscles simply act as strengtheners for various parts of the body. The abdominal wall is an example. Here nature created what has been called "the first plywood." Weakened by man's switch to upright walking, his abdominal cavity has a difficult job in retaining the intestines. To help, muscles have formed in layers whose "grain" runs at right angles to one another for additional strength. Man has copied this plywood technique in gluing together layers of wood, cloth, and so on to create materials of superior strength. Muscle works in this way in the diaphragm, which separates the upper and lower body cavities. Again, the evolutionary process is not complete, and occasionally the human machine breaks down in hernia of the abdominal wall or of the diaphragm, and man has to close the breach with surgery or external bracing.

Getting back to our drawbridge model, we lift its movable span to permit a ship to pass by pulling on a cable attached to the free end to cause desired rotation of the span about its hinges at the fixed end. In other words, we shorten the cable. This is how a muscle operates; it shortens itself and causes movement of the bone or other material it is attached to. There are about 650 muscles in the human machine, and each of them, whether it is the muscle that causes a smile, the lifting of a finger, or the beat of the heart, operates on this very simple principle of contraction. Most muscles work in opposed pairs, to provide movement in both directions.

To lift our drawbridge, a motor turns a shaft, let us say, and winds up the cable to shorten it for the desired movement of the span. Muscle has the ability to contract lengthwise when the proper electrochemical signal reaches it. This action takes place on an all-or-nothing basis; the muscle is in one of two positions, either contracted fully, or completely relaxed. Different degrees of movement are effected by different amounts of muscle being called into play. The muscle's action is analogous to that of an electrical solenoid. When a switch is closed, the solenoid's magnet is energized and this draws in a plunger that effects the desired mechanical action. Open the switch, and spring-loading returns the solenoid to its normal position. The solenoid uses electrical energy to energize the magnet; muscle uses energy stored from the food we eat.

Organs

Within the human machine are a number of organs vital to its proper operation; some of them vital to *any* kind of operation. We will begin with the heart. This organ, generally considered most important of all, if such a separation of functions is admissible, is essentially a pump. It is actually a double pump and several valves, interconnected cunningly to perform the task of circulating the blood through our body. This vital fluid approaches 10 percent of the body's weight. From one side of the heart the blood is pumped to the lungs, where it is oxygenated. Returning to the opposite side of the heart, the blood is then pumped into the arteries that carry it throughout the body so that the oxygen and other constituents can be deposited where they are needed. The spent blood is returned through the veins to the heart and the whole cycle is repeated. Failure of the heart for as long as four or five minutes results in death or at least permanent damage to the brain.

The lungs too are pumps. Operating like bellows, they draw in air from outside and make oxygen available to the blood as it circulates through the lung lining. To accomplish this transfer, the flat cells of the pulmonary alveoli provide a surface area of about five hundred square meters. The lungs must pump about ten quarts of air in and out each minute, and if they fail to operate for more than several minutes unconsciousness results, followed soon by death if oxygen is not forthcoming.

On its return trip from the way stations throughout the body, the blood is filled with impurities exchanged for the fresh supply of oxygen. These impurities must be filtered out, and this filtering is done in the kidneys. Within these organs (there are two as a safety factor, although man can get along with only one if necessary because of accident or illness), there is a maze of passageways that contain blood being purified. Through a process of osmosis in which part of the fluid passes through a membrane, urea is separated from the blood. Excreted from the body as urine this represents the biggest use of the water intake of the body.

The stomach and intestines perform the task of extracting energy-producing material from the foods we eat. The process is a combination of physical and chemical action. Aiding in digestion are the liver and pancreas; glands that produce "juices" necessary for breaking down foodstuffs.

The spleen is an organ that serves as a reservoir of blood in case of emergency. This is the organ we can most readily do without, and many have had it removed following accident and lived quite normal lives thereafter.

Of all machines, only the animal variety includes organs that serve to produce more of its kind. Man being bisexual, there are two kinds of sexual organs, or groups of same. The production engineer can only look wistfully at nature's method.

The Sensors

Man could not survive without a heart to pump blood through his body; but there would be little point in survival without a brain in working order, even though the body could live without that. The brain is a control center that is at once the envy and despair of the engineer. Comprising something like ten *billion* neurons, or nerve cells, and weighing about three pounds, the brain fills the cranium with pinkish-gray, spongy material folded intricately on itself to yield more area for interconnections between nerve cells. To it come nerve signals from eyes, ears, nose, and other sensors, and from it go impulses controlling the millions of tiny or gross actions necessary to the process of living.

In some manner that yet escapes the neurophysiologist and other interested scientists including cyberneticist and bionicist, this fantastic multiplicity of nerve interconnections also serves as a repository of information in the form of memory. Bits of information by the billions or perhaps trillions are stored in the brain to be called on as needed. The brain is also the decision maker, basing its judgments on information from the present environment compared against the background of experience stored within it. Like his hands, man's mind distinguishes him from the lesser animals, and from even the most sophisticated artificial machines he has been able to contrive. So awesomely complicated is the human brain that there are students of the subject who surmise that man cannot hope to comprehend its workings.

The operation of the brain, and the nerves that join it to the rest of the body, is electrochemical in nature. The brain's structure bears many resemblances to electrical and electronic circuits, and is in fact generally simpler in principle than these latter. In practice, however, it is far more complex than even the most advanced electronic devices.

The eye, one of the sensory organs bringing information to the brain, is a camera that is the envy of science despite any of the shortcomings that have been pointed out. True, it does not have the ability some man-made cameras have to see the infrared and ultraviolet realms of the spectrum. The eye is subject to lapses when faced with fatigue and extreme muscular strain. However, it registers in color and detail at a speed fantastic even compared with sophisticated photography techniques. It transmits "movies" to the brain with the "frames" so close together the effect is of continuous movement. It is capable of adjusting automatically to changes in light, and radically so in conditions of almost total darkness where it calls into play a new set of receptors. It has a built-in lens cover, which can close involuntarily in a fraction of a second to protect the delicate eye. Yet in spite of its delicate structure and fantastic performance, the eye is tough and durable, built to serve for periods of up to 100 years.

A somewhat less amazing organ serving to convey information of the outside world is the ear. Originally this "nerve" may have served simply to register pressure but through evolution it has expanded its purpose to record fluctuations in air pressure and thus is of greatest use in receiving sound stimuli. Like the eye, it is not capable of the broad range provided by some man-made devices. Human hearing encompasses vibrations of sound from about 30 cycles to something over 10,000 cycles per second, although with age this upper limit decreases. Some animals, dogs included, hear sounds far higher in pitch, in the ultrasonic range man must detect by artificial means.

In addition to its function as a receptor of audible information, the ear, or rather a portion of it, doubles as a balance mechanism to tell man when he is right side up. The ear sends signals to the brain to indicate whether or not man is level, and even furnishes clues that he is turning.

Man's nose is commonly thought of first as the organ he smells with, and surely life would be far less interesting without this nose for news of the aroma and odor world. However, at this stage of his evolution, man's nose is more useful as a breathing device, permitting him to take on air at the same time he eats and drinks, and also to breathe with his mouth politely closed.

The Skin

Without some kind of protective case for all these things, man would be an odd-looking specimen indeed, and not very practical either. Surrounding the basic skeletal framework, and the muscles, organs, and other internal materials and components, is the skin of the human machine. Flexible, durable, waterproof, and yet porous to permit necessary sweating, the skin serves to hold man together and to dress him up at the same time. Truly, beauty is only skin deep; few of us can view the exposed details of raw flesh, pulsing arteries, and flexing intestines with anything close to pleasure.

Aiding the skin in its protective function is our hair. At one time man was far hairier than now, to guard him against the rigors of a tougher life, and to warm him before he moved indoors. Today we get by with a thick mop on our heads and traces of hair elsewhere on our bodies. Hair has become largely a matter of vanity nowadays; we want it in ample quantities upon our heads, and often wish there was less of it in other places.

Another place where skin does not suffice in itself is at the ends of our fingers. Just as he needed teeth to chop up and grind his food, primitive man needed fingernails to claw his adversaries. At least, he once did. Now nails too are largely a matter of style and pride, to be kept scrupulously clean and sometimes to be painted cosmetically. More like bone than skin, finger- and toenails are probably a relic of the scales with which reptiles were covered, a not especially ego-building thought.

Artificial Man

Here then, in somewhat irreverent and overly simplified terms, is the human machine. Even the least of its functions tossed off casually in the preceding pages can only be regarded with envious wonder by the best of our engineers or technicians. Duplication of the human machine is a feat that will apparently be reserved for the Creator, although the indications are that men are going to try the awesome task some day.

For all its marvelousness, however, the human body is still a machine. Like a machine we build, it must have fuel to operate. It must have inputs and outputs of some sort to be useful. It must be capable of control. And it must obey the rules of nature, encompassing physics and chemistry and the other pertinent disciplines, just as man-made machines must. Because of these rules, the cyborg is possible; because it is possible, it exists. Let us see how many of nature's bits and pieces man has succeeded in copying, crudely yet successfully enough to be compatible with the original "natural" machine.

At the top of man's head is surely the simplest job of copying. The wig may be nearly as old as the crutch, and the man or woman wearing a wig is a cyborg to some extent though we may not consider this application of any great import. Likewise eyelashes, fingernails, and teeth. Man can implant living teeth, or he can substitute artificial teeth of metal or other material.

Just above the false teeth there may be a nose that has been altered by a human technician. The nose job is perhaps the most popular cosmetic surgery being done. There are other such beautifications or restorations. Ears have been rebuilt, or created almost from scratch. Lips, cheeks, whole faces, in fact, have been "made" by surgeons.

The female breast has been beautified by "uplift" operations, or simulated in some degree by surgery after operations to remove cancerous tissue. In some cases, even the nipple is provided, cleverly constructed of grafted skin.

The eye yielded to man's encroachment on nature hundreds of years ago when spectacles made their appearance. The result was a creature never before seen in nature. Eyeglasses restored to man part of his original visual ability. Such devices as telescopes, microscopes, jeweler's loupes and magnifying glasses provided vision exceeding anything in nature.

Corneal implants of glass and other materials have been tried. Contact lenses are a more intimate form of spectacles. Transplants of donor material are done by the thousands each year. Foreseen are techniques in which the eyeball is frozen and the cornea actually ground to a new and proper shape for correcting visual defects!

There is as yet no substitute for blood, but fluids have been developed that can be added to the bloodstream to build additional blood quickly for the patient.

The human machine has the remarkable ability to grow and to repair itself. Man cannot match this feat artificially but he can effect repairs on the body that nature is incapable of. He is also learning to modify and alter the basic machine so that it better fits the new environment surrounding it. At present these alterations are minor in nature, for reasons both technical and moral. But the possibilities are increasingly obvious. The basic Mark I human machine is susceptible to radical changes—hopefully all of them improvements.

5 *Artificial Outer Man*

A really mobile artificial arm and hand must use the missile techniques. But there are terrific engineering problems to be solved. A remote manipulator to handle atomic wastes demonstrated beautifully coordinated multiple controls. But it can weigh twenty tons in order to have all the engineering apparatus necessary to make its finely calculated motions.

There is no reason we can't make use of "outside power" in the manipulation of artificial fingers. But weights must be reduced to a small fraction of what is now possible, even if transistors are used to supply electric power. . . .

We need to externalize the controls connecting the machine to the man, to bring materials out through the surface of the skin that will permit skeletal attachments. This could make possible transplanting of limbs, and a Limb Bank. We may eventually know enough about growth processes to start experiments in regrowing human body parts.

Dr. John Lyman
Director, Biotechnology Laboratory, UCLA
1962

The most obvious cyborgs are those whose modifications show, that is, have been made on the outside. Eyeglasses, for example, or a hearing aid. A wig, a nose job or elevator shoes. These we class usually as trivial examples, although they are not that at all. More significant are cases like the wheelchair patient for whom wheels of metal and rubber substitute for the normal locomotion of limbs. Closer to a more complete restoration of function are mechanical braces that enable a polio sufferer to walk more or less under his own power and with some degree of naturalness. Finally, there are those humans in whom artificial devices take the place of a missing part.

Every year in the United States there are more than 100,000 babies born with skeletal defects. Six percent of all born have some kind of shortcoming. These blunders on the part of nature are the inescapable flaws that are a statistical part of genetic evolution. Such horrors as man's tragic misuse of drugs like Thalidomide are added to nature's mistakes. Hopefully, recurrences will be few, but with increasing use of potent drugs that can affect man genetically the possibility remains an ever-present danger.

For every baby born with a defect, however, there are nearly twenty who are practically perfect. Nature does get most of its products off to a good start; man himself succeeds in botching up far more of his fellows through automobiles, as mentioned earlier, and other accidents. Deaths are sometimes the merciful part of the story. The aftermath of crashes is the ward full of crushed and maimed: men with legs missing, women with horribly disfiguring burns, and youngsters with vital organs damaged or destroyed.

There is thus an obvious need for humanity to patch itself up. Having crippled one another with our stupidity and carelessness, the least—and most—we can do is try to put ourselves back together with some semblance of former appearance and ability. When war comes, the need is compounded. Even in the atomic age, there will be survivors of bomb blasts, and these may need more help than victims of old-fashioned lethal weapons. There is some consolation in the knowledge that as man's sophistication at warfare increases, so does his technological ability in the methods of restoration and rehabilitation.

In World War II, Secretary of War Henry L. Stimson pressed for a vigorous program of prosthetics research by the National Academy of Sciences–National Research Council. Known first as the Committee on Prosthetic Devices, it later became the Committee on Artificial Limbs and is now the Prosthetics Research Board.

The U.S. Navy formed its own Prosthetics Research Laboratory on Mare Island, near Vallejo, California. This facility has moved to Oakland, California. The Army too has its laboratory for artificial limbs. The Army Prosthetics Research Laboratory is situated in Forest Glen, near Washington, D.C., at the site of a former posh girls' finishing school. Naturally the Veterans Administration is interested in artificial limbs and has its own Prosthetics Center in New York City.

The year 1945 saw the foundation of the Biomechanics Laboratory of the University of California in San Francisco. Similar to the San Francisco laboratory is the Biotechnology Laboratory at University of California at Los Angeles, headed by Dr. John Lyman. There are prosthetic rehabilitation centers in Denver and in Chicago and New York. At Grand Rapids, Michigan, is the Child Amputee Center.

Helping not only Americans, but spreading the benefits of prosthetics developments around the world is the Institute of Physical Medicine and Rehabilitation, founded in New York by Dr. Howard A. Rusk at the New York University–Bellevue Medical Center. Rusk noted that while there were 17,000 amputees in the U.S. Army during World War II, there were 120,000 major amputations in the civilian population of this country in the same period, and that this condition prevailed around the world.

In 1961 the University Council on Orthotic and Prosthetic Education was formed, linking workers at UCLA, New York University, and Northwestern University.

The year 1962 saw the initial meeting of the Prosthetics and Orthotics Committee of the United States Committee of the International Society for the Rehabilitation of the Disabled. The function of this new group is to coordinate and strengthen United States participation in the work of the International Committee on Prostheses, Braces, and Technical Aids.

Mexico has a Rehabilitation Institute producing 1,200 artificial limbs a year for unfortunates in that country. It was founded by Romulo O'Farrill, Sr., a newspaper publisher in Mexico City who was aided following the amputation of a leg in the United States. Besides limbs, the Institute produces plastic noses, ears and eyes.

Prosthetic Devices

Prosthetics have been defined broadly as devices by which humans not only regain abilities they have lost, but also add new "unnatural" abilities. In this sense telescopes, bull horns and airplanes are prosthetic devices. More customarily the term is applied to the former application, especially in the form of artificial limbs.

The thought of amputation is repugnant and understandably so. It is instinctive to fear the loss of a limb; this is part of nature's survival mechanism. Mention of an artificial limb usually calls to mind a replacement with a frightening metal hook at its end. Part of this awe stems from the fictional Captain Hook, who wielded his sharp prosthetic "hand" as a horrible weapon. Another vicious character in fiction, Long John Silver, got about on a peg leg. It is unfortunate that the connotation of evil has thus become associated with the artificial arm and leg. Added to our natural squeamishness about such things, it has made acceptance of amputees a difficult thing, and particularly for the handicapped themselves.

The hook is of course a functional shape, and the newer double hook has proved itself efficient and foolproof. "A fake hand," says one doctor, "can't compare with a good honest hook." Wearers have been taught, and have taught themselves, a variety of skills that seem impossible. So successful is the prosthetic hook that its shape has been adopted in many of the remote-control devices designed to handle material and objects unsafe for humans to touch.

The Thalidomide tragedy put sharp focus on the need for artificial limbs for babies, but youngsters had demonstrated the effectiveness of prosthetics long before this. Six-month-olds have been fitted with simple "pylon" devices or even prosthetic hooks to take the place of missing arms. A two-year-old learned effective use of an artificial arm in just two days, and played happily with his hook and even a special baseball glove attachment.

Obviously the need here is for courage, patience and understanding on the part of the *adults* concerned. The child has the least problem of all. One baby, minus an arm and a leg, was provided with a jointless pylon wooden leg and a "passive" hand at ten months. Before the age of two it had graduated to a fully jointed leg and an artificial arm with a hook. Observed using them both expertly at thirty-two months, the child "vociferously resented having them taken off." Understandably so; any of us would resent losing an arm and leg even temporarily.

Even the youngster not trained from an early age to use artificial limbs can make the change gracefully if not as quickly. A few years ago a twelve-year-old boy fell into high-tension wires and lost both arms. Fitted with artificial ones at the Army's Forest Glen Laboratory, he learned to dress himself, eat his meals, and even to write again. It was found that his handwriting actually resembled his original penmanship, despite the loss of kinesthetic contact. This seemed to indicate that such skills depend on the eyes and the control centers rather than the sense of touch.

In this case, the boy had lost both arms completely; the artificial replacements were attached to his shoulders. Such an achievement cannot be fully appreciated by someone who has not faced the problem, but a bit of thought indicates the magnitude of the feat. Imagine both hands securely tied behind your back, and two inanimate, jointed objects strapped to your shoulders. Simply by moving your body, pick up a pencil and write your name. Or put on a shirt or get yourself a glass of water.

It requires motivation of the strongest order to succeed at this seemingly impossible task of coordination. Yet people succeed, just as others succeed in painting pictures by holding the brush in their teeth, or writing with their feet.

A missing hand is much less a loss. Here the person has an arm to furnish the power and do most of the positioning. In such cases he is often given an artificial hand that looks like the real thing. Of rubber and plastic, complete even to nails and fingerprints, these hands are custom finished by artists who paint in the veins to match the patient's own coloring. Workers at the Army's prosthetic clinic "donated" their own fingerprints for this realistic feature, and thus for the first time there is more than one set of identical fingerprints in existence.

Artificial hands may be had in a variety of types. A passive hand has naturally curved fingers that cannot move. Other models may be adjusted with the good hand so that objects may be held. Still others are capable of grasping, much as the standard hook does. Army experts consider the hook a more functional device than the artificial hand with thumb and four fingers. Most of the things we do with our hands can be done by prehension, the grasping or pinching movement of the opposable thumb and the first two fingers. In a "pinch" the thumb and one finger suffice, thus the double hook. Walt Disney's artists draw Mickey Mouse and his friends with but four digits; perhaps the artificial limb designers will produce a man of the future with but two or three.

There are many handicapped who still have limbs, but cannot use them. In the United States, for example, there are some 50,000 polio victims who cannot use their hands. One technique is to surgically "freeze" the thumb and fingers in a functional position. But in 1958, Dr. Kenneth S. Landauer developed a "hand motivator" to help such people. This motivator, designed and built by Dr. Joseph L. McKibben of the University of California, simulates a muscle in the forearm. Consisting of a length of rubber tubing enclosed in nylon fiber with a special geometric pattern weave, the "muscle" is placed on the outside of the arm between elbow and the knuckles of the hand. It is connected to splintlike attachments on thumb and two fingers. Carbon dioxide gas is supplied to the rubber tubing by means of a switch and valve arrangement.

To operate the hand motivator, the patient places the immobile hand over the object to be grasped, and touches the valve with the other hand. As gas inflates the rubber tubing, the surrounding nylon material shortens in the lengthwise direction, pulling on the splints on thumb and fingers. These digits close on the object. To open the hand, the gas pressure is released.

A similar idea had been used by engineers at North American Aviation in 1955 to build a hydraulic arm motivator for a fellow engineer struck down by polio. This was operated by foot pedals, and even though it was cumbersome permitted the user to perform many useful tasks with his otherwise helpless arms.

Americans have no corner on the development of new and better artificial limbs, of course. As early as 1956, Professor Sigmund Weil and technician Otto Hafner at Heidelberg had developed pneumatic artificial arms powered by carbon dioxide as was the hand motivator in this country. Built of wood, metal and rubber, the device did not merely actuate the patient's own limb; it *was* the limb. Tested on fifty patients, the Weil-Hafner device allowed them to perform a dozen different movements. With it they were able to eat and drink, grasp objects firmly or gently as desired, use the typewriter, handle keys of another kind and to write with a pen. At a cost of from $350 to $600 the patient was fitted with a suitable arm and trained in its use for a period of three to four weeks. The pneumatic arm operates as long as two weeks on one cartridge of gas, at which time a recharge is necessary.

An early artificial hand was purportedly developed by workers in Ireland in about 1600. Unfortunately, three men were required to operate it, because it was so low in efficiency. The Army's work has been toward more efficient devices, since even recently some have delivered only 7 percent and required so much force to operate that they were often broken by their straining users.

Newer models have boosted efficiency to 80 percent, and the advantages of this ease of operation are obvious.

Although users of artificial limbs have proved they can perform many tasks successfully without "feeling" in their prosthesis, this element of touch is important and much work has been done to provide it or at least something resembling it. One clever idea involved placing a small balloon on the artificial finger, and connecting it with a similar container of air attached to the patient's chest. The idea was that pressure of the artificial finger against an object would result in inflation of the balloon against the patient's chest with resultant activation of nerves of touch in that area. Unfortunately there were "bugs" in the scheme. Another attempt used a buzzer that sounded on contact. This was to be interpreted in the user's brain as a substitute for a sense of touch. Researchers found that there is a "hardware tolerance" in most patients beyond which it is not wise to go. Perhaps some successful substitute for the sense of touch will be developed, but meanwhile it does not seem too much of a handicap even when totally absent.

A variety of powered artificial upper limbs are making their appearance now. In addition to pneumatic and hydraulic devices there are electric-powered models. One clever electric elbow is actuated by the patient's breathing. Of course in many cases the patient's own muscle, routed to the replacement limb by cables, does the actual work. This system, however, does not permit the delicacy of movement required for precise hand movements. For some time researchers have dreamed of using the faint electrical signals from nerves to actuate the artificial limb, and apparently success has been achieved in this amazing method.

In his novel, *Limbo*, Bernard Wolfe in 1952 described a weird world of the future populated by "vol-amps," or voluntary amputees. Their replacement limbs were described as follows:

Number One: the element he was holding now, he explained, was the socket. This was fitted permanently into the stump by cineplastic surgery, connected up with all the muscles and nerves of the stump.

Designed so that any kind of limb could be snapped into it and immediately be hooked in with the musculature and the neural system. . . . Number Two: the atomic-energy capsule, the power source of the mechanism. The movements of the limb were guided and controlled by the neural impulses relayed from the brain through the central nervous system, but were powered by this built-in plant. Which made the artificial limb infinitely stronger than a real one. . . . Number Three: this gadget, consisting of a wire coil and a metal rod which moved in and out of its electrical field, was a solenoid. Translated electrical into mechanical energy. Equipped with a system of levers and linkages which did the work of the original muscles and tendons, but with much more power and control. There was a solenoid for each muscular unit of the original leg; one in the thigh, one in the calf, one for each of the toes. In the arm, of course, the setup got a lot more complicated. . . . Number Four: all these tiny objects were thyratron vacuum tubes and transistors. Hundreds of them in each limb, laid out in relays they converted neural impulses into electrical ones to operate the solenoids. . . . Number Five: the oleo-strut shock absorber, in which compressed air, oil and springs were combined to cushion the impact of a fall. . . . Number Six: the gyroscopes, which controlled balance. . . . Number Seven: the strain gauges. Attached to pads on the fingertips, they duplicated the sense of touch by converting pressure into neural impulses. . . . Number Eight: the thermocouples, which converted temperature stimuli into neural impulses. . . . Number Nine: the cooling system . . .

"Efficiency!" the lecturer said. "That's the point. With real limbs, the maximum amount of work the human organism can put out over a sustained period of time, say for an hour or so, isn't much more than one-sixth of a horsepower. But with these self-powered jobs you can sustain indefinitely a level of work amounting to dozens or even hundreds of horsepower. Because the power doesn't come from your body, it comes from the energy capsules. All your body does is direct that power. Man, in other words, finally K.O.'s the machine by incorporating the machine into himself! At last we've got the answer to EMSIAC—the machine that incorporated man into it. Isn't that something, kids . . . ?"

Limbo describes the war that continues between the Free World and Russia, with a fierce competition in prosthetic devices. At an Olympic competition the Russian athletes, fitted with limbs far better than their opponents, walked away with the show.

A few years after this fictional glimpse into a cyborg world, the Russians seem to be living up to prophecy as far as prosthetic prowess is concerned.

With the sophistication of electronic equipment and devices, it is possible to identify and amplify individual tiny voltages produced in nerves by signals from our brain. Electroencephalographers have done this for some time in charting the electrical activity of the brain and of individual portions of it. Now the idea is being applied to those nerves leading to the patient's extremities. It is in Russia that the most success has been achieved, and that country's remarkable new electronic forearm has been reported by Mr. Charles Yesalis, vice-president of S. H. Camp Company, which specializes in orthotic devices. Yesalis led a group belonging to the U.S. Prosthetics and Orthotics Committee on a visit to the Russian laboratories.

Moscow's Central Scientific Institute of Artificial Limbs and Rehabilitation has developed a new hand consisting of a leather cufflike shell with a polyvinyl chloride coating resembling human skin. Inside the device is a complex electronic circuitry, storage battery, electric motor and associated gear mechanism. Weight of the artificial hand is about ten ounces, the same as a real hand. Work on the device began in 1958 when scientists A. E. Kobrinsky and V. S. Gurfinkel began to investigate the idea of control by electromyographic signals.

By 1959 the Russians had completed a test model of the artificial hand that passed clinical and technical trials. In 1961 production models were produced and have since been supplied to patients. A period of six to eight weeks is required to train users in proper manipulation of the new hands. Generally no difficulty is experienced since the device responds to the existing natural habit of movement. The fingers may be clenched and unclenched, weights of up to about ten pounds lifted, and delicate tasks such as writing and screwing light bulbs in and out of their sockets are possible. The artificial hands, including the training by a technician, can be bought on instalment payments. The storage battery supplies power for about three days of normal operation and then must be recharged. This is conveniently done overnight. The Russian workers claim they are now extending their technology to fabrication of a complete arm, fully jointed and capable of making circular movements, and even providing a sense of touch plus sensitivity to temperature!

A later chapter will discuss the technique of exploiting the body's own "myoelectric" signals to operate artificial limbs—and to do far more intriguing tasks. This phase of cyborg development is one of the most promising, and hints that gadgets described in *Limbo* may not be so far-fetched after all.

Man has need for artificial lower extremities too. Once a crutch or peg leg was the best that could be done, but in recent years substitutes approximating real legs and feet have become available. The road from early wooden legs to today's lightweight models was made possible by scientific study of the dynamics of human legs in action, and the application of mechanical techniques borrowed from industry. From the Germans came the idea of attaching a leg by means of suction rather than belts and harnesses. A new foot, called the SACH, for "solid-ankle, cushioned-heel" provides much greater walking comfort.

Plane-maker John Northrop put some of his engineers to work on artificial limbs during World War II. Applying aircraft techniques led to use of Bowden cable, a flexible cable encased in a protective metal housing, for controls. Also adapted from aircraft factories was the idea of light plastic laminates to replace wood or metal.

Hydraulic legs were designed and built, and here the interchange of ideas worked the other way. An oil seal developed by a prosthetics engineer for a hydraulic limb also found use in aircraft, including the P-38. Another hydraulic leg, an amazing advance that permits the walker to put all his weight on a bent leg, was developed by two German World War II scientists who came to the United States after their country's defeat.

Hans Mauch, who helped design the V-1 rocket for Hitler,

and Ulrich Henschke, who was also a German scientist, were brought to this country as part of "Project Paperclip" in which the U.S. Army recruited willing experts from their homeland. Mauch worked for 12 years at the Air Force's Wright Field, but in his spare time he tinkered with a completely different kind of project. With Henschke, a cancer researcher at Cornell, Mauch perfected the "swing and stance control system" that is the key to the new artificial leg.

Not surprisingly, many artificial limb engineers are themselves amputees who became interested for personal reasons. Among these is Howard D. Eberhart, who as an engineer on a project for the B–29 bomber lost a leg in 1944. He teamed with the man who amputated his leg, Dr. Verne Inman, and the two have contributed greatly to the improvement of artificial limbs.

Another phase of prosthetics work concerns artificial hip sockets and ball joints like the Smith-Moore type made of the metal vitallium. Here is a much more intimate mating of living and nonliving materials, yet many of these permanent implants have been highly successful and suggest even more daring techniques, such as bringing the patient's bone out through the skin for permanent attachment of an artificial limb.

Grafting Living Material

Far better than an artificial hand or arm of course, is a real one. Recently surgeons have succeeded in reassembling accident victims in miraculous fashion.

Man's big toe was once an opposable digit, like the thumb, and surgeons have successfully amputated big toes and grafted them onto the hands of patients lacking a thumb. Other toes have served as substitute fingers, and a farmer who lost four fingers in a threshing machine had four such new "fingers" added!

Plastic surgery, on the congenitally malformed and also on victims of accident and illness, has reached a high state of development. Not only new noses can be constructed, but complete new faces, although the process is anything but easy. Time- and patience-consuming, such operations take skin from other parts of the body for grafting where required. A very interesting variation of this technique is sometimes used to create an ear for a person lacking one.

Cartilage, obtained from the patient, or from a donor or bank, is diced into small pieces, placed in a plastic form the shape desired for the new ear and placed in an incision in the patient's stomach. After about two months the mold is removed and the cartilage framework—now fused into a single unit—is removed. The cartilage is grafted to the flesh on the head and allowed to attach itself firmly in place. Then further graftings of skin flaps are done to provide a covering for the new organ, and there is the ear.

Metal plates in the head are a commonplace. More recently bone grafts have been used to construct large sections of new skull for victims of accident or congenital deformity. Fleshy areas are padded out with synthetic material inserted in skin flaps. Surgeons can reconstruct or add muscle to rectify everything from sagging faces to inoperative sphincter muscles in the anus.

The reattachment of a living nose or finger is a dramatic enough operation but now it is possible to graft a hand, arm or even a leg back onto the body. Before long the grafting of a donor limb from a corpse may be successful. Attempts have been made, and much learned about the technique. Further work in suppressing the immune reaction will undoubtedly lead to common substitution of limbs in such cases. In this field the Russians claim the distinction of having grafted dozens of heads onto dogs (one at a time, of course!) in the last several years. In a more drastic operation, they have cut a pair of dogs in two and stitched up the unmatched halves of the animals.

The term "grafting" is used to describe the joining of living tissue. We are familiar with grafts of trees and plants; even such oddities as trees that yield oranges, lemons and grapefruit from a single trunk. When we cut ourselves, even if the wound is large, the severed parts will grow back together in time and if treated properly. Transplants are grafts, then, and generally referred to as one of four different types. These are "autotransplants," "isotransplants," "homotransplants," and "heterotransplants." If the surgeon shaves skin off our back side to patch a burned place on our arm, this is an autograft. Transplantation of a kidney from one to the other of identical twins is an isograft. A homograft involves the transplanting of a piece of bone from a human donor to another human not related to the first. And finally, a heterograft is the transplantation of say the liver of a chimpanzee into a man.

The complexity of the task obviously increases as we go from *auto* to *hetero*. The reason for this is nature's protective mechanism known as the immune reaction. This is a living thing's resistance to a foreign body, and protects us against infection by germs and viruses that would harm us. It is hard to quarrel with this defense device, although it should be pointed out that nature does slip up sometimes and carry this protection to ridiculous extremes. The nuisance called hay fever, and other allergies, are the immune reaction "protecting" us from orange blossoms or whatever it is that irritates. Sometimes we seem to be allergic to ourselves, and tragically a mother's body can react violently to the "foreign" baby in her womb.

Two methods of combating the immune reaction come to mind. First, if the cells of the patient match those of the donor, there will be no battle when they are joined. Knowing that identical twins have cells whose chemistries aren't antagonistic, researchers have gone on to show that less closely related people often have cells close enough to a match that transplants "take." Some authorities think that it may be possible to categorize people as to cell type, in a fashion something like the A, O and other blood types.

Failing at matching the cells, there remains a second method: destroying the immune reaction. For some transplants this drastic treatment poses no great problem. Bone, nerve, cartilage and other tissue can be irradiated to kill the lymphocytes that do battle with foreign bodies, and thus "take" successfully when grafted to a quite different cell-type patient. Drugs are also used, preparations called Imuran and the like. Hypothermia, the cooling of living material to low temperatures, is sometimes effective. Because the spleen and lymph nodes produce the antibodies, these are sometimes removed. The thyroid is removed in some cases as well as the thymus gland, and anticoagulants are resorted to.

We have not yet attained the prosthetic state of the art Wolfe envisaged in his novel, nor are living spare parts stocked in banks of limbs so that human bodies can be repaired like cars after a wreck, as suggested in popular articles on the subject. But there is a grain of truth in both these fictional and factual suggestions. One worker in the prosthetics field describes the attachment of various artificial limbs to a single universal socket permanently fixed to the wearer as the "Tinkertoy" approach. Different limbs may be snapped in place for different jobs. Here is reality quite close to the fictional "Limbo" technique.

And while the limb bank does not exist as yet, hardheaded experts in the field like Dr. John Lyman speak of the possibility of "growing" replacement limbs. Thus there are two ways to go in the substitution of limbs for the cyborg of tomorrow. Or maybe three, by combining growing and grafting techniques with electronics and hardware to make an even better replacement limb. As with the myoelectric idea, the subject of growth of living material in the laboratory warrants fuller treatment in a later chapter.

6 *Artificial Inner Man*

There are those who would argue that we scientists should have no concern for the effect that our discoveries will have on a society. My answer to that is simply that we too are members of society and as such have an obligation in this regard. Hence, I must conclude that it is my strong recommendation to the membership that positive action be taken to develop a code of ethics—a modern Hippocratic oath, if you will—to guide us in the use of artificial organs to sustain human life.

> Dr. Belding H. Scribner
> President, American Society for Artificial Internal Organs
> 1964

Along with replacements for the outer man, there is also a need for substitute parts inside our bodies. Heart trouble, kidney disorders, stomach trouble, and the ravages of cancer are among the ailments that take their toll. Until very recently there was little or nothing doctors could do in such cases. Then came new developments that dramatically improved the chances of those plagued by internal disorders. We can divide these developments roughly into three categories: first, new surgical techniques, particularly for the repair of heart damage; second, transplantation of substitute tissue, including whole organs; and third, the use of artificial organs to fill in for the patient's own during an operation, and sometimes for much longer periods.

In each of these methods, man's intervention leads to a new kind of human, produced not entirely by nature but partly by man himself and different to some extent from other men about him. While new surgical techniques often merely patch up a defect, remove useless tissue, and so on, they sometimes change the "plumbing" of the patient, or the structure of an organ itself. Faulty hearts are redesigned and intestinal tracts botched up by nature or otherwise are rerouted to permit satisfactory function.

Even the most radical of such operations seems conservative treatment, however, compared with transplantation technique. It is one thing to snip out an ailing or damaged piece of intestine or artery and stitch the ends back together; it is something else to insert a piece of living material borrowed from elsewhere in the patient's body, from a living donor, or from a tissue bank. More amazing are artificial parts taken "from the shelf."

Transplants

Bone grafts, and the transplanting of nerves and blood vessels using donor material were once revolutionary operations. Today they are commonplace. Doctors have moved on to the transplantation of whole vital organs. Early attempts failed because of rejection of the graft by the "host" but by thwarting the immune reaction even homografts and heterografts have been made to work.

Hundreds of kidneys have been transplanted. Beginning with identical twin transplants, doctors have moved on to close-relative donors, other human donors not related at all, and finally animal donors. The kidney is made easier to transplant because as little as 10 percent efficiency on the part of a substitute organ may suffice. The heart, however, must operate at nearly top efficiency to sustain life for any length of time.

Donor kidneys are often transplanted in a different area from the normal location, and new "plumbing" methods resorted to in removing the urine produced.

From 1955 through 1963 there were 244 kidney transplants. By 1958, a kidney transplant patient had a baby and in the same year the first nonidentical kidney graft was made. Whole-body radiation in great doses was resorted to, and a woman patient survived for 28 days, far past the time she could have without a substitute kidney.

In the years that followed, more and more nonrelated transplants of kidneys were made. Through 1963, 21 of 28 identical twin transplants were still alive. Five related donor transplants were still alive, but only one of 120 nonrelated donor operations survived more than a year. Late in 1963, however, doctors moved with desperate boldness to heterografts. Kidneys from a chimpanzee were transplanted successfully in a New Orleans Negro named Jefferson Davis. So well did he progress that he was permitted to return home for Christmas. Used on Davis to kill the immune reaction were the drugs Imuran, actinomycin C, azaserdine, prednisone, and also X-ray irradiation. Perhaps because his disease immunity was also reduced, Davis caught pneumonia and died on January 6, 1964, after two months. His kidneys from the chimpanzee were still functioning, however.

An earlier, less publicized similar operation at Charity Hospital in New Orleans also ended in the death of the patient, but on the day that Davis died, another transplant involving kidneys from a lower animal took place, this time at the University of Colorado Medical Center. Davis had been forty-four, the patient in Denver was forty-five. The donor was a baboon rather than a chimp.

While the kidney is the most-transplanted of the organs, it is not the only one doctors are learning to substitute. In Denver, where the baboon kidneys made medical history, doctors also performed a liver transplant on a middle-aged bachelor named William Grigsby. The liver was taken from a man who had just died of a brain tumor. Grigsby's own liver was being eaten away by cancer.

In Denver, too, surgeons transplanted the spleen from a mother into the body of her young son. In Mississippi and in Pennsylvania, lung transplants were made. Stomach transplants have not been made; however it is usually possible to make drastic changes on the patient's own stomach, cutting away large portions of it, and reattaching it to the intestine in operations for cancer, ulcers, and other disorders. New tracheas have been substituted in humans, some directly from donors, some from banks of human spare parts, and some from cow and other animal donors.

Until 1964, transplantation of the heart remained a feat performed only in the laboratory on animals, particularly in Russian laboratories and on dogs. The surgeon Demikhov has become a master of this technique, and describes no less than twenty-four different ways in which to install a replacement heart in an animal. Extra hearts have been transplanted, giving the dog two pumps for his blood supply. All this research obviously is practice for similar transplants in the human. However, in his book *Experimental Transplantation of Vital Organs* published in 1962, Demikhov makes no claim for a human heart transplant.

In January, 1964, surgeons at the University of Mississippi Medical Center in Jackson transplanted a chimpanzee's heart into a human dying of heart disease. There was no alternative but such a heterograft. For an hour the new organ beat and kept the man alive, then death took place because the chimp heart was not large enough to pump a sufficient quantity of blood. However, the attempt had been made, and "clinical success" achieved. Other operations would surely follow.

The Russian Voronoff made history years ago by transplanting testicles in aging men. Russian doctors today claim far greater success than their notorious predecessor. World War II provided injured men to work on, and the Russians claim that victims who lost their reproductive organs had been operated on and made whole again, even to the extent of being able to gratify the urge for sexual union. One patient is claimed to have survived with his transplanted organs for 19 years. American experts are admittedly skeptical of these operations.

Artificial Organs

The concept of artificial organs goes far back in medical history. When a doctor attempted the cross-circulation treatment of Pope Innocent VIII described earlier, he was hinting at the use of artificial heart and lungs. Dr. Carrel's work with the perfusion of organs outside the body bordered on such substitute organs. And in 1912, J. J. Abel, L. O. Rountree, and B. B. Turner published a paper in the *Journal of Pharmacy and Experimental Therapy* entitled "On the Removal of Diffusible Substances from the Circulating Blood of Living Animals by Dialysis." Dialysis is the separation of substances by diffusion through a membrane, a kind of selective osmosis. Electrodialysis serves industrially to remove salt from water, for example.

A man can live a week or more without kidneys. He can live three days with no liver. But without a heart and lungs his survival time drops to a few minutes. The heart, obviously, is the most vital of our organs and also the most difficult to provide a substitute for. Because heart and lungs are so closely tied in their purpose and operation, early substitutes were a combination of both.

In 1934 Dr. John H. Gibbon started up the first artificial heart-lung machine. Carrel and others had come close to this, using mechanical pumps for blood and substituting living lungs outside the body in experiments. However, Gibbon's machine and the later Read-DeWall "oxygenator" were completely artificial. Blood is taken from the patient and pumped to a tank. There it is carried around on a metal drum in a thin film exposed to the air. In this manner it rids itself of carbon dioxide and oxygen is taken in as in a real lung. Other oxygenators are "bubblers" in which gas is bubbled through the blood to effect the exchange of oxygen for carbon dioxide. Another oxygenator is the membrane type, which more nearly duplicates the natural action of the lungs.

The heart-lung machine makes it possible to ease the strain on overworked living hearts. Researchers at Harvard Medical School proved that the machine could reduce heart attacks in dogs. Human subjects can be similarly helped. Routing the blood around a damaged heart via the heart-lung machine also permits an operation on the stopped heart that would be impossible otherwise.

There are other uses for the machine. For example, cancer can be treated with dramatic results. With a large portion of the patient's blood supply circulating through the machine, the part of the body harboring the cancer can be heavily perfused with killing drugs that eliminate the parasite. To attempt such a drastic method with the harmful drug circulating throughout the entire body would be fatal. Perfusion of localized tumors has been successful with melanomas affecting the legs, lungs, breast, liver, colon, pelvis and even the brain.

Later heart-lung machines have been greatly improved over the pioneer machine. Smaller units that are more efficient and more dependable are produced, and disposable units have become available. However, even the most compact heart-lung machine is intended as a temporary substitute only. Much more development was required if something approaching a replacement for the human heart was to be realized.

Forerunners of a complete artificial heart were component parts for that organ. Artificial arteries had been an accomplished fact for some time before the technique was applied to the aorta, a large artery directly attached to the heart. It is frequently subject to "aneurysm," or weakening of the walls and subsequent ballooning of the artery. This is but a prelude to hemorrhage and death. Einstein died of an aortic aneurysm, refusing an operation to repair it. Surgery involving living tissue as a replacement had been done but there was a need for a readily available artificial substitute.

Dr. W. Sterling Edwards of Birmingham and Dr. James S. Tapp of that city's Chemstrand Corporation teamed to produce the first practical artificial aortas. Others had experimented unsuccessfully with paraffin-lined glass tubes, silver- and gold-plated aluminum tubing, and other materials. Edwards tried nylon tubing, but found it lacked the needed flexibility. With Tapp he developed methods of braiding nylon fibres, using such homely equipment as an old tie-knitting machine and a shoelace braider. The new material worked and the Edwards aorta graft looked like a small-diameter vacuum cleaner hose, the bellowslike shape permitting all the flexing necessary.

In tests the new graft retained its strength inside a patient for many months. It caused no reaction from natural tissue, and apparently was long-lived. Today there are thousands of people whose blood courses through a large, Y-shaped aortic graft of nylon.

Besides the aorta, the valve in that artery too was replaced with an artificial device. Made of Lucite plastic, the valve body was equipped with a plastic ball inside that moves back and forth to act as a check valve, much like the item you buy at the hardware store to permit hydraulic flow in only one direction. Early models had the disadvantage of being quite noisy, but adjustments have resulted in suitable aortic valves. Other artificial valves use "leaves" of plastic. Some people have as many as three artificial heart valves.

Medical students have long been familiar with the fact that an electric wire implanted in a turtle's heart keeps it beating long after the turtle dies. The idea of a similar trick with an ailing human heart was natural. In 1952 Dr. Paul M. Zoll of Beth Israel Hospital invented an external pacemaker. This instrument was placed on the chest, over the heart, and from 50 to 60 volts of induced electricity jolted the patient's ailing muscles. Even for adults, however, this treatment was hard to take and children were terrified of it.

A number of researchers, one of them an electronics technician who was himself a heart sufferer and desperately trying to find a way to save his own life, experimented with better ways to do the pacemaking job. The result, too late to help the technician, unfortunately, was a smaller, lower-voltage package, mounted outside the patient's chest, but with wires running through an incision so that electrodes could be implanted in the cardiac muscle. One early user, Carl Barker of AC Sparkplug's engineering department, made his pacemaker adjustable so that he could slow his heartbeat to a comfortable 60 to 70 beats a minute while he slept, and speed it up to a stronger 90 when he was up and around!

The externally worn pacemaker was a lifesaver to many, but it was not as handy as it might have been. There was the danger of severing the vital life-giving wires accidentally, inconvenience during bathing, and so on. In 1960 the first completely implanted pacemaker was placed inside the chest cavity of Mrs. Rose Cohen of Brooklyn. Fitted with tiny mercury batteries that would last several years, the new pacemaker was a great improvement. Thousands of users in the U.S. and the rest of the world owe their lives to these artificial heart prodders. Even the prospect of being opened up again periodically for battery replacement is no great deterrent, since the operation is a minor one requiring only a local anesthetic. More recently interest has again turned to the external, wireless pacemaker, however. Also being experimented with are pacemakers powered mechanically by the muscles or even by natural electricity generated by the body.

Going beyond the simple pacemaker idea, some doctors have sought to create a natural "second heart" of diaphragm muscle wrapped about the aorta and stimulated with a pacemaker. Similar to this idea is an implanted artificial second heart, snapped in place in two sections about the aorta and generating its own electricity from pressure on piezoelectric crystals contained in it.

Experimenting on dogs with such implants, researchers discovered a danger in the implanted receiver picking up the wrong external signal and beating to the wrong cadence. Nevertheless, dogs with electronically sparked diaphragm-muscle hearts have lived for as long as a year.

Another heart problem is that of high blood pressure. Here again the artificial organists are at work. It has been found that the carotid sinus nerve in the neck affects blood pressure, and artificial regulators or "baropacers" have been implanted in the necks of human patients. Two types of baropacers are being tried. One taps electric signals from the heart by means of implanted electrodes and routes these signals to the carotid sinus. The other baropacer uses implanted storage batteries and its own electronic timing mechanism to control blood pressure.

Because waning storage batteries in such devices necessitate a minor surgery for replacement, researchers have developed a technique in which the storage batteries are recharged from outside by induction.

Replacing the complete human heart with an artificial one has long been the dream of artificial organists. Dr. Kolff, of Cleveland Clinic's Department of Artificial Organs has been engaged in this work for many years. In 1957 he enlisted the aid of White Motor Company, Stewart Warner, Bendix Aviation Corporation and Westinghouse. Starting with a fuel pump from a White truck, Kolff got busy.

The heart is a fantastic pump, as may be imagined. The truck pump had a capacity of about one quart a minute, an appreciable flow of gasoline. But the heart must pump *five* times that much blood. With a magnetically operating heart using plastic sacs squeezed by oil pressure, Kolff succeeded in keeping a dog alive for two hours with his early trials. This was an externally powered heart, to be plugged into a socket, or driven by a portable battery.

In 1958 Dr. B. J. Kusserow of Yale University installed a pump, driven by an electric motor, in a dog's stomach. Seven inches long and less than three inches in diameter, this unit took the place of the right side of the animal's heart. It was made of Lucite, with a rubber diaphragm and steel accessories. Powered from outside the body, the partial heart featured a variable pumping rate, and kept dogs alive as long as 10½ hours.

By the early 1960's more than half a hundred firms were doing work on artificial heart valves, and many individuals, institutions and firms were seriously tackling the problem of the complete artificial heart. Such a project, obviously, is not a simple one. Dr. Kolff found that the proper motors, solenoids and other components did not exist. He and his assistants designed the solenoid they needed, thus advancing that technology. "Mixmaster" type pumps were experimented with, but did irreparable damage to the blood. Piston-type pumps were designed, including unique alternating pumps. Kolff believes that his group's "sac-type" heart, which simulates the action of a real heart, is a promising design.

Pulsating air pressure squeezes a sac within the Cleveland artificial heart, much as heart muscle does in the genuine article, expelling blood for circulation. This type has been successfully used in calves for periods up to thirty hours.

In developing this heart the Cleveland Clinic had the help of NASA researchers who suggested a pump powered by air or other gas instead of electricity. Another space-age technique was used when a capacitor in an artificial heart was made by applying a layer of the same aluminized plastic used in the Echo satellite.

Dr. Kolff is confident that the implantable artificial heart is close at hand, and waiting only the proper time and patient for its trial.

It was Dr. Kolff who in 1945 completed the first successful artificial kidney. The kidney was a large machine consisting of a stainless steel tank and cellophane tubing (sausage casings!). Blood taken from a patient suffering from uremia or renal poisoning circulated through a cellophane membrane wound about a metal drum and immersed in a bath of water. Waste material in the form of molecules small enough to pass through pores in the cellophane was carried off by the water, and the purified blood then returned to the patient. The machine performed much the same function as the human kidney, in removing urea from the blood. In addition to eliminating metabolic waste from the blood, the artificial kidney also performed another function of its living prototype in that it regulated the acid-base balance or pH factor of the blood by removing sodium and hydrogen ions.

Since the war, the artificial kidney has been greatly improved. Smaller and more efficient types were developed, and "throwaway" or disposable kidneys made their appearance. And their uses have increased. It was found, for example, that not only uremic poisoning but aspirin and barbiturate poisoning could be fought successfully. Radioactive strontium 90 is removed by the artificial kidney and thus prevented from being deposited in the bones. In one amazing application, schizophrenics have been treated and shown great improvement, indicating that mental disorders may stem from certain organic imbalances.

Normal kidneys circulate some 1,700 quarts of fluid a day to produce about 1½ quarts of urine. In the artificial kidney the doctor can regulate the flow of blood through the cellophane tubing and also control the temperature and content of the water bath and thus make the "kidney" do what he wants it to do.

Originally used as a temporary assist to the patient until his own kidneys could recuperate, the artificial organ has come to be a way of life for many victims of kidney trouble. Seattle's Washington University and Swedish Hospital has an Artificial Kidney Center that treats a number of patients on a continuing basis. These people, who otherwise live and work like normal human beings, spend a night or two a week in bed at the hospital, "plugged in" to the artificial kidney by plastic fittings implanted in their arms or legs. More recently, a larger "monster" kidney has served several patients. So wonderful is the job the machines do that there are far more people pleading to be accommodated than the hospital can handle.

Besides this drawback of equipment shortage is the high cost of treating those for whom there is room, and the taxing moral question of how to select those who will live if they have access to the artificial kidney. A board of anonymous Washington citizens passes on all candidates.

Present cost is between $5,000 and $10,000 a year per patient. The Veterans Administration plans a large-scale operation handling perhaps 300 patients per kidney center. Ideally, a replacement human kidney is sought. But there are never enough, and as yet the immune problem has not been solved. Uremic poisoning kills something like 100,000 a year. With an artificial kidney of the proper materials there is not the drawback of rejection by the patient. A more hopeful development is an "implantable" kidney.

Dr. Peter Salisbury has made small implantable kidneys and used them successfully in dogs. Substitute kidneys of all sorts have been investigated, including even the use of one of the patient's lungs as a "lavage" site to purify the blood! Salisbury suggests using a part of the abdominal cavity, as has been tried in dogs. This kind of lavage, plus an implanted artificial kidney, may one day be successful in humans.

Complicated as the kidneys and heart are, man has succeeded in artificially duplicating them to some extent. It is doubtful if he will have the same success with liver, spleen or other organs. Dr. Kolff has reported on an artificial pancreas that worked in the laboratory for a dog. This was a "bench setup" in which a commercial autoanalyzer was connected to the dog's bloodstream and regulated injection of insulin from an outside source as needed. Whether or not extension of this idea to an implantable device, and its use as replacement for thyroid, adrenals and other endocrine glands is feasible, remains to be seen.

A technique that may be possible with artificial internal organs is the removal of the patient's own and their repair "on the bench," installing a spare while such work is done. Perhaps it will be better merely to leave the artificial spare inside the body and return the repaired heart to a whole-organ bank!

Associated with artificial organs are the artificial interconnections being used to install these replacement parts as well as to repair damaged blood vessels. Prosthetic devices of metal and plastic, incorporating attachment techniques like those used in plumbing of a more artificial kind, are commonplace now. Instead of laboriously sewing the ends of arteries together, the Russians have developed a special stapling machine. Other techniques used fittings that clamp ends together, with "teeth" to dig into the tissue. More recently, new epoxy cements are being used to glue blood vessels and even bones! Patients who need periodic artificial kidney treatment are sometimes permanently fitted with metal or plastic couplings.

American Society for Artificial Internal Organs

In 1954 a new medical society was formed: the American Society for Artificial Internal Organs. Since 1955 it has held annual conventions at which the "artificial organists" describe their work in this startling new field. The *Transactions* published by the society read more like fiction than science, and it is obvious from reading them that we stand on the threshold of a new world of implanted artificial organs made of metal, plastic, and other materials in some ways superior even to the marvelous cellular structure of our bodies.

Largely through the efforts of Dr. Peter Salisbury, who had been active for a number of years in work with artificial organs, the American Society for Artificial Internal Organs was formed. Its first meeting was held at Atlantic City. The reception of the new medical group by their colleagues was not exactly heart-warming. As a member would later recall, "Ridicule was painfully evident. It was incomprehensible to many doctors that the artificial organists could take themselves so seriously. People just tittered, confessing that the name of the new society called up the idea of mechanical organs of reproduction."

Despite the snide comments of their fellows, the handful of ASAIO members held their conference and a number of papers were presented. "Only a few of the more fantastic papers were deemed unpublishable . . . ," said Dr. Salisbury. Judging from papers that appeared in the *Transactions*, those refused must indeed have been fantastic. Among the published:

"Heterologous Lung; Its Use as an Ultrafilter in Animals and Humans"

"Microsurgery—Application to Organ Transplantation"

"Artificial Heart in the Chest; Preliminary Report"

"Considerations and Calculations About the Optimum Solenoid to be Used for an Intrathoracic Artificial Heart"

"Experimental Replacement of the Mitral Valve with a Flexible Polyurethane Foam Prosthesis"

"A Simple, No-prime, Pumpless Artificial Kidney"

By the 1960 meeting Dr. Salisbury could optimistically tell 160 members:

> . . . we have come quite a way since the meeting in 1957 when the subject of intracorporeal implantable artificial organs was first mentioned and was greeted with very mixed feelings and with the remark that the difficulties were comparable with a trip to the moon.
> It seems that we may have intracorporeal organs before we actually get to the moon. Maybe the Russians will arrive at the moon first and we will have the intracorporeal artificial organs first.

By 1961 the society had overcome most of the objections, ridicule, and disbelief. It then boasted 170 members, including many in foreign countries. Dr. Charles K. Kirby in his presidential address proudly stated:

> In some ways we have even achieved a certain aura of respectability. We no longer have to meet near the periphery of this seashore resort. . . . We have now moved up to the fashionable part of the board-walk. It has become possible to mention the name of our society, during casual conversations, without evoking bizarre emotional reactions. When I receive mail addressed to the society, the mailmen deliver it like any other mail, without even a trace of that quizzical sly smile. . . .
> I believe that we can construct successful artificial internal organs before the tissue barrier obstructing organ transplantation can be overcome.

Other progress was made that year too, and editor Dr. George Schreiner could announce, "We are happy to state that the new *Index Medicus* will include the 'Transactions' among the smaller and more select list of journals which are currently indexed."

Referring to this changed attitude on the part of the rest of the profession, one artificial organist quoted the "seven ages of ideas" of Dr. C. Walter Lillehei, professor of surgery at the University of Minnesota:

1. *The idea state: "Won't work; it's been tried before."*
2. *After successful experiments with animals: "It won't work in men."*
3. *After one successful clinical patient: "Very lucky. Doubt if patient really needed treatment. Too bad. A tragedy, really, because now they'll continue."*
4. *After 4 or 5 clinical successes: "Highly experimental, too risky, immoral, unethical. I understand they've had a number of deaths they're not reporting."*
5. *After 10 or 15 patients: "They can succeed occasionally in carefully selected cases. But most patients with the defect don't need the operation anyhow."*
6. *After large series of successes: "So and so in Shangri-la has been unable to duplicate their results. I hear a number of their patients are dying later deaths."*
7. *The final stage: "You know, this is a very fine contribution, a straightforward solution to a difficult problem. I predicted this. In fact, in 1929, I had the same idea. Of course, we didn't publish anything, nor did we have penicillin, cortisone, and fine anesthesia in those days."*

There was evidence of continuing acceptance at the tenth annual meeting of the ASAIO, held in Chicago April 12 and 13, 1964. Sixty-six new members were admitted to the society, bringing the total to 293 doctors representing the profession in the United States and 16 other countries. More than 80 papers were presented, with titles like the following:

"Further In Vitro Evaluation of the Army Heart Pump"

"Studies on the Artificial Heart Driven with Controlled Gas Pressure Device on the Pressure Generator for Universal Use"

"A Small Ventricle-Type Pump for Prolonged Perfusions; Construction and Initial Studies, Including Attempts to Power a Pump Biologically with Skeletal Muscle"

"A New Dynamic Disposable Artificial Kidney"

"Long-term Operation of an Electronically Controlled, Plastic, Auxiliary Ventricle in Conscious Dogs"

"The Piezoelectric Artificial Heart"

"An Improved Bioelectric Generator"

Delivering the presidential address was Dr. Belding H. Scribner, who spoke on the ethical problems of using artificial organs to sustain human life. His words were especially meaningful, since Dr. Scribner spoke to his audience "as a patient as well as a physician because I am looking at you through donated corneas and therefore feel a very personal debt to a society which permitted the evolution of eye banks and willed eyes which makes the donation of corneas possible."

One sad note in the ASAIO *Transactions* for 1964, yet a stimulus to increased effort, was the black-bordered announcement of the untimely death of Dr. Kirby, former president of the organization.

In his concluding remarks Dr. Scribner pointed out that the moral and ethical guidelines we have inherited are becoming more and more inadequate. On the religious aspects of birth and death control, he said:

Some theologians argue that it is against God's will to control birth and death. Could it not be equally well argued that one reason that God gave man intelligence is because He realized that if man were to survive on this planet, he would need that intelligence to be able to control, voluntarily, his numbers—something that no other living creature has the ability to do.

7 The Brain

I wheeled the table with the encephalograph close to the vessel which contained the brain and fastened the five electrodes to the cortical tissue. One near the right ear, two high on the forehead, one above each eye cavity. . . .

I switched on the current that drove the small motor, which in turn, drew out a white paper slip an inch per second at a frequency of sixty cycles. A pen scratched a faint line on the moving paper. I amplified the infinitesimally small currents the brain was sending until their power was great enough to move the pen.

On the paper strip the activity of Donovan's thought processes showed in exact, equal curves. The curves repeated themselves; the brain was at rest, not really thinking now. The pen drew smooth alpha curves, concise as breathing.

I tested the occipital lead. The deflections were continuous, ten cycles per second, with very low seven to eight cycles per second waves.

I touched the glass and at once the alpha waves disappeared. The brain in the glass was aware that I was standing there!

Delta waves appeared on the moving strip, a sure indication that the brain was emotionally disturbed.

It seemed fatigued, however, and suddenly it fell asleep again. I saw the repeating pattern reappear. The brain slept deeply, its strength exhausted by the grave operation.

I watched its depthless slumber while the pattern of this sleep, drawn by a pen on white paper, slipped through my fingers.

I watched for hours. I knew I had succeeded.

Donovan's brain would live though his body had died.

Curt Siodmak
Donovan's Brain
Jonathan Cape & Harrison Smith, 1942.

Of all our organs the most awesome is the brain. The idea of mechanical substitutes that duplicate the actions of our bodies —steam shovels, weaving looms, and other "scattered fragments of ourselves"—causes the rank and file to toss its shoes into machinery and inventors into the nearest lake. But the notion of machines that think, and thus *control* the other devices we build rouses even greater horror—not just in the minds of the displaced manual laborer but the intellectual as well, since now he too faces displacement by a contrivance of semiconductors, ferrite loops, and thin-film circuitry. It is the artificial brains in the heads of R.U.R.'s robots and Ambrose Bierce's chess player that stir revulsion in our souls. Comfortingly, the brain is the most complex of all our organs and one that may never be truly approached by an artificial substitute.

Fictional literature is filled with stories of the transplantation of brains. An example is Siodmak's book, *Donovan's Brain,* in which a living brain is neatly excised and later set up *in vitro* in a laboratory much as Carrel actually did with the lesser organs.

Doctors have grafted whole limbs. Kidneys, hearts, livers and other organs even including the reproductive have been stitched into men with varying degrees of success. But no one has yet transplanted a living brain or implanted an artificial brain. Dogs' brains have reportedly been kept alive in the laboratory, but the nearest approach yet made by neurophysiologists to the brain transplant operations described in fiction was announced in 1964 at Cleveland Metropolitan General Hospital. There Dr. Robert J. White successfully removed the living brains from rhesus monkeys and kept them alive for periods up to 18 hours in the laboratory. Supplied by an artificial heart-lung machine with fresh blood from a monkey blood bank, the isolated brains were instrumented for electroencephalograph measurements. Apparently the monkey brains were still able to hear and "respond" to sound and sight stimuli.

These actual experiments indicating that an isolated brain can be aware of the outside world sound like those of *Donovan's Brain* brought to reality. In the book, the doctor experiments first with a monkey. This was a Capuchin rather than the rhesus used at Cleveland General. From there the fictional researcher moved up to a human brain, and the question now is how long that step will take in real life.

Thirty-five years ago, J. D. Bernal wrote prophetically:

. . . *channels of communication are already at hand in the electrical nature of nerve impulses. The brain thus connected up continues existence, purely mental and with very different delights from the body, but even now perhaps preferred to complete extinction.*

Announcement of the limited success of these operations points up the great technical difficulties yet to be overcome before an excised brain can be transplanted, or perhaps used to operate an artificial system. The shocked response of the public to the announcement emphasized the other great barrier to work in this direction: the resistance on moral grounds to what many consider ghoulish goings-on.

This is not to say that there are no mental cyborgs, for it is in this department that man has done most to artificially supplement that with which nature endows him. Even a scratchpad and pencil amplify man's brainpower mightily, and it is interesting to note that computers usually incorporate a "scratchpad memory" in their electronic circuits.

While man has greatly extended his mentality artificially, his brain remains much as it was a thousand years and even ten thousand years ago. It will remain little changed ten thousand years hence, *if* the changes are left to genetic evolution. Man will not leave them to nature, of course. He has already begun to tamper with his think box. But this task is not so "simple" as analogous operations on the heart, kidney, or liver.

British physiologist Sir Charles Sherrington referred to the brain, in reverent awe and perhaps some frustration, as the "great ravelled knot." It is that, certainly. From every part of the body there converges a network of nerves tunneling up through the spine and burgeoning into the mass of brain cells. An estimated ten billion neurons make up the modest weight of the gray matter. The sheer size of such numbers is appalling to the would-be artificial-brain maker. At a penny each, ten billion switches would cost $100 million, and he would still have to pay someone to solder from two to one hundred interconnections to each! None of us could afford an artificial brain duplicating our own. Such figures make the high cost of artificial kidney plug-in treatment seem a pittance by comparison.

Surgical Alteration

Another famous knot was tackled not by unravelling, for that approach was seen as hopeless by Alexander the Great. He solved the problem of the Gordian knot with a single stroke of his sword, and to this day the most of what man has been able to do in altering the brain's mechanism is an approximation of Alexander's drastic surgery. The prefrontal lobotomy, or "leucotomy," of brain surgery is a far cry from science fiction's brain doctors who probe with tiny needles to burn or cut "bad connections" in neural circuitry to create a superbrain, or at least one which permits its owner a life of pleasant thoughts.

Work on the artificial heart is prompted by the knowledge that this organ heads the list in the causes of death. Brain disorders, however, incapacitate more people than all other causes combined. Our ancestors had their mental troubles, even when life was still lived quite close to the nature that produced them. Today man's environment is one that nature did not foresee. Nature's rate of change is not fast enough to fit man for life under new pressures. Religion, psychiatry and psychology do not seem to be halting the increase of mental disorders. In desperation man is looking to other, more drastic methods.

Anthropologists have shown that such brain surgery goes far

back in history. Thirty thousand years ago early neurosurgeons hacked holes in their patients' skulls and chopped inexpertly but perhaps with great effect at the neuron mass laid bare.

Will Durant, in *Our Oriental Heritage,* says this of the early art:

Trephining of the skull was practiced by primitive medicine-men from the ancient Peruvian Indians to the modern Melanesians; the latter averaged nine successes out of every ten operations, while in 1786 the same operation was invariably fatal at the Hôtel-Dieu at Paris.

A hundred years ago a blasting accident performed a similar brain operation on a New Englander that left him a "changed person" with regard to personality. Some time after that, in this century, actually, sincere effort was begun in the direction of surgical alteration of the brain.

In 1933, Drs. John F. Fulton and Carlyle Jacobsen at Yale Medical School removed the prefrontal region of the brains of two chimpanzees named Becky and Lucy. Following this surgery, it was found the chimps had changed radically in their personalities, although their mental ability seemed unimpaired. Once subject to tantrums and frustrations, now they merely shrugged if they made an error.

Just as monkeys preceded men into orbital flight, so Becky and Lucy were the front runners for human patients in the field of brain surgery. By 1936 a Portuguese doctor named A. Egaz Moniz, with the help of surgeon Almeida Lima, began similar lobotomies on fifty hopeless mental cases in Portugal. Moniz received a Nobel Prize for this work in 1949. Lima severed the connections between the prefrontal lobes and the thalamic region of the brain. Such leucotomies (from the Greek *leukos* for white, since it was a white tissue severed by Lima) produced dramatic results with the patients so altered. Dementia victims and schizophrenics showed marked benefit, and more than half of such operations were termed successful.

Within a year, leucotomies were attempted in the United States and thousands of such operations have since been performed. However, with time have come serious second thoughts about the benefits. To be sure, psychotic tendencies have been removed or alleviated. But balancing this is the appearance of other negative personality traits: increased selfishness, deterioration of the sense of moral responsibility, lack of foresight, bad manners and emotional instability.

High on the list of bad effects are loss of imagination and the increase of poor judgment in leucotomy patients. Psychologist Ward C. Halstead, in a twelve-year study following the introduction of the surgical technique in 1935, reported that "the frontal lobes, long regarded as silent areas, are the portion of the brain most essential to biological intelligence."

Brain Waves

The neurosurgeon of prehistoric ages apparently charted his course by guess, gosh, and intuition. More recently brain men have resorted to "electrical prospecting." The early Romans knew about electricity in living things, and reputedly even used the torpedo ray in a primitive form of electric-shock brain therapy. Luigi Galvani, a latter-day Roman, rediscovered natural electricity serendipitously with laboratory frogs' legs strung on a wire.

In 1870 two Prussian army doctors, Fritsch and Hitzig, walking through the casualty-strewn battlefield at Sedan, put Galvani's experiment in animal electricity to a ghoulish test. With electric shocks they touched parts of exposed human brains and noted the involuntary twitchings thus produced in the battered remains of the soldiers. Among the things these strong-stomached researchers learned was that electric shock to one side of the brain produced movement of the *other* side of the body. This discovery has two very significant implications.

First, nature cleverly evolved a brain that protected living things with this division and reversal of control. Assume a caveman fighting a saber-tooth with a club or spear in his right hand. The tiger rakes the man's head and damages the brain on the right side nearest him. If that side controlled the right side of the body, the caveman would be finished. However, his right arm is guided by the protected left side of his brain and he may thus live to fight another saber-tooth and sire youngsters whose brains are so wired!

Second, there is the implication that if the brain controls by means of electrical impulses, external impulses can effect an approximation of that control. We already have electrical control of humans to some indirect extent with radio and television. The other kind, more direct and sure, may come in time.

Elaborating on the battlefield extemporizations of the Prussians, Victor Horsley electrically mapped the areas of the cortex responsible for the movement of various parts of the body and also the areas where signals to the brain from the body were received. And in 1875 English physician R. Caton discovered that the brain itself produces currents of electricity. Looked at from our vantage point in time, Caton's discovery seems childishly simple. He—and others of his day—should have known that this was the case. Or should they? The human heart produces a good big jolt of current in the cardiac pacemaker, but the production of electricity in the brain is on a tiny scale. Sending a message generally takes less energy than digging the ditch the message tells us to dig, and the brain deals only in signals and not in carrying out physical tasks.

In 1928 Hans Berger introduced the technique of placing small electrodes at various places on the outside of the head to record the electrical currents produced. Electroencephalography, or "electrical brain-writing" was born. By 1934 Lord Adrian and B. H. C. Matthews demonstrated the "Berger rhythm," the regular rise and fall of electrical current that can be interpreted to indicate the state of the brain.

In Caton's day there were no electronic amplifiers to boost an almost undetectable electrical signal so that it could be measured precisely. By the 1930's there were such amplifiers. Adrian and

Matthews soon established that the 10-cycle-per-second Berger rhythm came from the visual area of the occiput of the brain, and not from the entire brain as Berger himself had thought.

Since then the electrical prospectors, armed with what amount to neurological Geiger counters, have done an admirable job of charting the brain. Shock treatments have proved effective in some cases of brain disorder. Russian electronic machines are claimed to induce sleep artificially. With animals, and even human subjects, researchers have demonstrated that it is possible to effect movement of the various parts of the body to some extent with electrical stimulation. Other significant discoveries have been made.

ESP, or extrasensory perception, is a well-known psychological term. More recently scientists have been investigating something called ESB, the electronic stimulation of the brain. Far more demonstrable than ESP, the new technique also has much more potential for influencing our mental future.

In 1954, Dr. James Olds of the University of California at Los Angeles reported on studies made on rats in the laboratory. Using implanted microelectrodes, researchers learned of the existence of what they call pleasure centers in the brain. Making it possible for the rats to administer mild electric shocks to their own brains, Olds and his associates were surprised to see the animals give themselves as many as five thousand shocks in an hour, forgetting all other creature comforts including eating while so doing.

At Yale University, Dr. José Delgado and others have also studied ESB and achieved startling results in another direction. Permanently implanting electrodes in the brains of animals including monkeys and cats, the Yale workers learned that they could control the actions of the animals by stimulating specific areas of the brain. Timid monkeys were turned into fighting furies; cats were made to cringe in a corner at the approach of mice. Animals could even be made to freeze rigidly under proper stimulus. Control was effected by plugging wires into the attached brain socket, which contained as many as six different electrodes.

Or it could be done remotely by radio signals, with power supplied by small storage battery packs mounted on the animals.

Principally a tool for study of abnormal mental behavior, ESB seems to have important implications in this field. It might also make possible an electronically robotized human, automatically controlled by the programmed timer attached to him, or by signals sent from "headquarters" by radio. At an electronics symposium held since the development of ESB, an engineer discussed the possibility of the unscrupulous implanting of such control gadgets in infants soon after birth. Here would be the ultimate in government control. There are, happily, pleasanter prospects for the application of electronic stimulation of the brain.

The nerve signals arriving in the auditory area of the brain are interpreted by the brain as sound. The signals reaching the visual area of course register as sight. These specialized interpretations or translations occur even if the stimulus did not originate as sound or sight. Electrical stimulation of the auditory nerve, for example, has been found to produce a "sound" in the subject's brain. Such a signal is crude noise and nothing more at this stage of refinement of the stimulation technique. Stimulation of visual nerves with a mild electric shock produces analogous flashing lights in the brain, somewhat like the display we can produce simply by pressing on our closed eyelids.

A clue to what is going on in those with mental disorders or nervous disabilities may have been found in victims of epilepsy. Patients have reported on occasion that immediately preceding an attack they can "smell" a foul odor, "hear" sounds or "see" sights that do not exist. Cells adjacent to the pertinent nerves are hyperstimulated chemically or some other way, and cause phenomena interpreted as smell, sound or whatever in the brain.

A few subjects have even demonstrated the ability of "tactile" sight. Simply by feeling an object, they can tell its color. There is thus the possibility of feeling sights, seeing sounds, smelling pressure and so on, in which a person handicapped visually might "see" through other channels. Allied to this phenomenon is the "neurophone," an electronic equipment recently invented by a teenager and allegedly able to convey sound directly to a human brain with radio waves. Suggestive of mental telepathy, clairvoyance, second sight, thought transference and other such phenomena, such a device would make possible entirely new concepts and applications of the brain.

Descartes had his own ideas for improving the mind. In his *Discourse on Method* he wrote:

> *The mind so strongly depends on temperament and the disposition of the bodily organs, that if it is possible to find some means which will make men generally more wise and more clever than they have been till now, I believe that it is in medicine one should seek it.*

More recently, J. D. Bernal in *The World, the Flesh and the Devil* echoes much the same sentiment in pointing out the intimate interrelationship of mind and body:

> *Altering in any perfectly sound physiological or surgical way the functioning of the body will certainly have secondary but far-reaching effects on the mind . . .*

Depending as it does on oxygen for survival, the brain may be affected by the supply it gets of that element. In the old and in some cases in the diseased, the blood supply to the head is curtailed because of an accumulation of material in the blood vessels, the so-called hardening of the arteries. Dissolving this "sludge" may speed up circulation. More recently some doctors have devised a technique of forcing a special catheter through the clogged vessels. Fondly known as the "roto-rooter," this device is designed to clean out the body's plumbing much as the plumber uses the mechanical tool to do the same for artificial plumbing.

Sleep is a strange phenomenon that seems more vital to the brain than food to the body. During sleep the brain dreams, an act apparently caused by relatively random connections of the nerve nets of memory and thinking. Yet some men, among them those like Edison, required hardly any sleep compared with the eight hours most of us must average. Could we produce a race of nonsleepers whose minds could accomplish that much more with an additional eight hours each day to function?

Artificial Brain

The mechanics of the human brain, or rather the electrochemistry of that organ, is basically quite simple even though it would be foolish to say we can duplicate it. The circuit along a nerve is either on or off, the same two-valued arithmetic or logic employed by most electronic computers. Thus the brain is a digital device, although physiologists are sure there are important analog undertones present.

The idea of ten billion interconnected switches is something to give even the most sophisticated information theorist fits. However, Dr. W. Grey Walter, one of Britain's leading neurophysiologists, takes a more enlightened view of this multiplicity. To his notion, there are nowhere near that amount of "perceptible functional elements" in the human brain.

A million interconnected cells yield discrete states, or "bits" of information amounting to the quantity $10^{2,783,000}$, a fantastic number that, if strung out as a 10 followed by the requisite number of zeros, would fill a number of volumes this size. Dr. Walter estimates that all 10 billion cells thus interconnected would store as much information as there are particles in the universe as defined by Sir Arthur Eddington! Thus a relatively few nerve cells of artificial nature would seem to be sufficient for a substitute for our brain.

He sees perhaps one thousand functioning centers. This would seem to reduce the brain to the level of a quite ordinary mechanical calculator, but the mechanics of binary mathematics is deceptive.

As Dr. Walter points out, one thousand on-off switches interconnected in all the various ways possible could store up the life experiences of all the men who have lived until now, and who will live for the next billion years. Thus his version of the brain's switching arithmetic is realistic and quite plausible. Nature is famous for overdesign, or redundancy in many of her devices. Would she be apt to provide ten billion elements when the ten-millionth part of that number would do the trick? The answer would seem to be yes. Consider the quantities in which a male human produces sperm, and compare this fantastic number with the number of children he produces.

The brain, therefore, may be a machine operating reliably at only a tiny part of its potential, and man may one day learn how to boost his mental capacity far beyond what we consider genius today. Yet, paradoxically, straining our mentality only slightly often results in hopeless frustration and sometimes severe mental breakdown. Our brains, marvelous though they be, are prone to some hard-to-understand shortcomings, particularly in the field of logical decision making.

As a practical beginning, Dr. Walter set about designing electronic robots named Elmer and Elsie, equipped with only two such elements. These small, wheeled robots, fitted with photocell eyes, performed in amazing fashion, negotiating their way about obstacles, staring at themselves in a mirror, or at each other in a fashion that prompted the name *machina speculatrix*.

From Elmer and Elsie Dr. Walter evolved another electro-mechanical creature dubbed *machina docilis*, the name arising from the fact that this one could be taught, whereas Elmer and Elsie went through life only as smart—or stupid—as the day they were born. *Machina docilis'* name was Cora, for conditioned reflex analog. Using four elements to the earlier machine's two, Cora learned to respond to whistle blasts, kicks and such signals. Walter describes circuits in Cora labeled Insight, Amnesia, Reminiscence, and other human-sounding characteristics. Cora's memory resembled that in humans in that it faded with time. There were also defense mechanisms and inhibition circuits. Cora demonstrates the possibilities of a four-celled brain.

Electronic computers far outrace the nimblest minds in the handling of figures. Much of this is because of the inherent speed of the switching components involved. Present-day computers operate at nanosecond speeds, that is, in billionth parts of a second. Foreseen are machines in the picosecond range, a thousand times faster than those now in use. Man's puny neurons, however, fire at the relatively snail-like speed of milliseconds, or thousandth parts of seconds.

Speed is not all of the answer, however. Among humans are those who can calculate with lightning rapidity. Not as fast as electronic computers, but at such speed as to make normal human performance ridiculous. Such feats as almost instantaneously finding the square of a six-digit number are typical.

In May of 1964 an unusual case of such mental ability was reported at the American Psychiatric Association convention. Identical twins twenty-four years of age, so retarded that they could not do simple addition or subtraction, were able to determine almost instantly the day of the week for any date over a range of 2,000 years. This performance of the "human perpetual calendar" compares with a mathematician's time of 10 to 15 minutes, using formulas.

Such freak performances are generally considered no indication of intelligence, and most of those possessing these remarkable abilities seem able to do little else with any distinction. However, the electrical wizard Steinmetz could recall logarithm tables from memory, and aerodynamicist Theodor von Kármán could multiply six-digit numbers in his head at age six.

It is as though the brain circuits in some of us are connected in such a fashion that complicated mathematical answers are as implicit as they are in an electronic computer. The question of logic problems is an intriguing one also. We are familiar with such puzzles that keep us awake all night at times, yet the solution may involve only three permutations of two-valued reasoning and can be done almost instantaneously on simple "logic machines" made of cardboard. Some humans instinctively arrive at right answers.

Could this be accomplished in *all* of our brains with a bit of judicious "rewiring" or educating of networks?

For that matter, is the speed of the human brain unalterable, or might it be boosted by artificial means? Dr. Walter points out that an increase in the "alpha rhythm" (which seems to be an indicator of the brain's metabolism) from 8 cycles per second to 13 cycles enables the driver of a car moving at 50 miles an hour to stop it 5 feet sooner.

Despite all the effort spent in trying to fathom the brain, and all the talk of artificial brains taking over, this organ, the master tissue of the race, in all likelihood will be last to be replaced with either a transplant from another human (surely not from a monkey let us hope!) or from the electronic laboratory. The artificial kidney exists as hardware. So does the heart. There apparently is no similar artificial brain being built by members of the American Society for Artificial Internal Organs, or by any neurological society or computer manufacturer. Man's electronic brain for a while yet at least will not fit him like a helmet, with fine platinum leads piercing his scalp. He will be connected to it more tenuously as he sits as a programmer at a high-speed computer and feeds information to it and reads the answers it spews back to him at a thousand printed lines a minute. This coupling, undramatic as it seems, is still a sophisticated form of the superbeing under discussion here, the cyborg.

8 Myoelectric Control

There is a second class of machines with which we have also been concerned which has a much more direct and immediately important medical value. These machines may be used to make up for the losses of the maimed and the sensorily deficient, as well as to give new and potentially dangerous powers to the already powerful. The help of the machine may extend to the construction of better artificial limbs; to instruments to help the blind to read pages of ordinary text by translating the visual pattern into auditory terms; and to other similar aids to make them aware of approaching dangers and to give them freedom of locomotion.

Norbert Wiener
The Human Use of Human Beings
Houghton Mifflin, 1950.

The term "mechanical man" is understandable in view of the many mechanical principles the human body makes use of in its operation, and in preceding chapters we have discussed in some detail the mechanical devices that help create the artificial or semi-artificial man. In what we have discussed there have also been hints at a more subtle approach to coupling man and machine. The fact that the nervous system operates somewhat like an artificial electrical control system suggests a fascinating new approach. In an age of electronics it is logical that this new science be put to work with living systems that are susceptible to the flow of electrons.

Electricity has two main uses in artificial systems: as a control, and as a source of power. We may roughly divide body electricity into the same two categories and we will look at them in this order, taking the idea of nerve "signals" first.

Myoelectric Signals

In 1963 poet Robert Graves of Oxford and Majorca delivered the Arthur D. Little Lecture at Massachusetts Institute of Technology. In his talk, which concerned his wish to discover the mystique behind modern science, Graves applauded "Dr. Norbert Wiener's brilliant use of severed nerve-ends to give a man whose leg has been amputated control of an artificial one." This tribute touched off a controversy concerning research at MIT and Harvard on the use of "myoelectric signals" to operate prosthetic devices, a sophisticated cyborg technique already exploited by Russian workers and described briefly in an earlier chapter.

John Lear, science editor for *Saturday Review*, noted Graves's mention of Dr. Wiener's cybernetic application wedding man and machine. Lear himself was aware of such experimental work going on, having discussed it with Wiener a year earlier. However, he had withheld mention of it in his science columns because of the highly experimental nature of the work, and the feelings of Wiener and others involved that such disclosure before publication in a scientific journal would compromise the men working with myoelectric artificial limb applications. Now that mention *had* been made of the work, and distorted mention at that, Lear felt justified in commenting briefly on Graves's address and setting the record straight.

True, Dr. Wiener should have been applauded for the feat, but mostly for encouraging a younger scientist, Dr. Melvin J. Glimcher, associate professor of orthopedic surgery at Harvard and director of the orthopedic research laboratories at Massachusetts General Hospital. Glimcher typifies the new breed of cyberneticist, or bionicist, combining knowledge of physics and mathematics with mechanical engineering and biology. His doctorate is in biophysics.

Researching the literature on artificial limbs, Glimcher came on descriptions of a British type incorporating "feedback" principles stemming from cybernetics. However, this device did not operate very successfully. A better prosthetic hand seemed to have been produced by the Russians, and Glimcher made a trip to Moscow to see it used and be further convinced he was on the right track. Impressed with the Russian myoelectric hand, Glimcher returned to this country determined to design and build a better one.

Enthusiastic, he visited Dr. Wiener, who was then laid up in the hospital with a broken hip sustained in a fall. Wiener was impressed by Glimcher's project and suggested men who would be valuable on the team.

Half a dozen of the people involved in the project took strong exception to Lear's article, pointing out he was raising false hopes in amputees—even though Lear plainly credited Glimcher only with *probably* picking up signals from a nerve, and pointed out that actual use of these signals to operate an artificial limb might be decades away. And there the controversy rested. Dr. Wiener died shortly thereafter, before he could see the flowering of this phase of the science he launched some two decades ago.

As with Sputnik, the Russians seem to have stolen a march on their American scientific brethren in the field of myoelectric control. Like Mr. Yesalis of the S. H. Camp Company, who was quoted earlier as saying that the Russian device did indeed operate as its inventors claimed and that it was the only such artificial hand he knew of, Dr. Glimcher was much impressed. Lear had written that Glimcher considered the Russian hand crude, but the letter of protest signed by Glimcher, Wiener and others refuted this, and said that despite some technical difficulties it was more advanced than any similar device they were aware of. Surely the father of cybernetics should be quite cognizant of developments in his own field.

The Russians refer to their hand as a "cybernetic forearm prosthesis activated by muscle nerve impulses." Such a method is obviously far superior to such techniques as cineplasty, in which the patient's muscle mechanically operates a cable. The Russian's claim their system "is most convenient because the command is transmitted from the cerebral cortex to the hand by the beaten track which was severed by the trauma." Simply "thinking about it" operates the hand.

When the brain signals the hand to move, the muscles to be used produce a tiny change in electrical potential at the site. Electrodes of metal foil glued to the skin over the muscles can detect this change in voltage and measure its amplitude. Given this basic signal to work with, Kobrinsky and Gurfinkel used it in the manner described in a Russian document:

> *The information obtained from the continually measured bioelectrical potentials of the muscle is processed into a set of standard impulses whose repetition frequency is proportional to the power of the biocurrents.*
>
> *To reproduce any movement, biocurrents are tapped from two antagonistic muscles, for instance, flexor and extensor, and accordingly two channels of converting the information are used. As a result two groups of program signals are simultaneously fed to the input of the servodrive.*
>
> *The servodrive which carries out the program of control is a mechanical step motor operating in the differential regime, a condition allowing for control with biocurrents from two antagonistic muscles. . . .*

Interestingly, in 1964 it was reported that Germany's Thalidomide Trust was negotiating for rights to quantity production of the Russian myoelectric limb in Germany.

While the Russians were achieving this success, American researchers were also busy. At UCLA's Department of Engineering, Drs. Weltman, Groth, and Lyman published a report entitled "Analysis of Bioelectric Prosthesis Control" in 1959. Well aware of the benefit in using the patient's own nerve signals to control an artificial limb, researchers were simply not able to extract reliable signals from the welter of myoelectric activity present in the body.

Instrumentation was one of the problems. Placing of electrodes of metal foil above the pertinent nerve area was generally successful in picking up tiny electrical signals, but the slightest movement of the electrode relative to the body introduced false signals. New, lighter, and better-attached electrodes were designed and eliminated this part of the difficulty.

In August 1962, an International Symposium on Application of Automatic Control in Prosthetics Design was held in Opatija, Yugoslavia, and the UCLA scientists presented a paper entitled "Electrical and Mechanical Properties of New Body Control Sites for Externally Powered Arm Prostheses."

Application of the myoelectric control idea to another field came about this time. Astronauts were being hurled into space, and while the bugaboo of weightlessness seemed little problem, there was much concern over man's ability to operate controls properly during the extreme acceleration environment of blast-off and reentry. At times these forces reached as high as 8g, with the result that a man's body "weighed" more than half a ton, and his arm alone might weigh close to 100 pounds. Lifting such a burden and using it precisely is an impossibility, so the idea of tapping myoelectricity to operate a booster for the arm was a natural.

Working under contract to the Air Force, Spacelabs, Incorporated, a California firm, got busy on the design and construction of a myoelectric "muscle booster" for astronauts and others subject to extreme conditions of acceleration. Results of this work were detailed in a paper presented at the third Bionics Symposium, held in March, 1963, at Wright-Patterson Field, Dayton, Ohio. Authors were Drs. Weltman, Martell and Sullivan, and Dean Pierce of Spacelabs.

The researchers investigated the myoelectric signals available in an average-size muscle and found that the total "bandpass" was from 3 to 1,000 cycles per second, with maximum signal power in the region from 10 to 200 cycles per second. The amplitude of the signals ranged from 1 to 3 millivolts, about 1/1000 the voltage in a flashlight cell.

Only the voluntary contraction of a muscle can be successfully detected; relaxation signals are buried in electrical "noise" always found at the body's surface. Two kinds of muscular activity result in myoelectric signals at the detecting electrodes: normal muscular activity, and learned or trained activity.

Electrodes were glued in place over the anterior deltoid, medial deltoid, and posterior deltoid, and also the pectoralis muscle. A training period of only one or two minutes was found sufficient for the subjects to effect control of the servo booster.

Subjects were trained to use the myoelectric boost system to operate a switch on a simulated spaceship control panel. With the arm artificially weighted to 80 pounds, the subjects carried out their tasks successfully, proving they could effect in and out movements simultaneously with up and down. Speed of the booster was normally 6.8 degrees per second and no difficulty was experienced at this slow rate of movement. Above 13.5 degrees per second subjects were unable to hold the hand steady at the desired position, and the booster displayed "oscillatory hunting" of a type common in electromechanical equipment.

Another use of myoelectric control is in the training of muscles in the rehabilitation of patients. Since electrical signals can be displayed visually on an oscilloscope or audibly heard on a loudspeaker, a subject can see or hear when the proper signal is being generated. Although the sound from the loudspeaker is simply so much noise, it is interesting to speculate on the possibility of using voluntary myoelectric signals to permit a speechless person to "talk."

Much of the difficulty reported by American scientists working on the problem of using electromyographic signals for control of artificial limbs continues to be the distinguishing of the desired signal in the midst of all the "noise" or irrevelant electrical activity surrounding it. A sneeze, for example, might raise havoc with a piece of equipment monitoring muscles for control functions. However, progress is being made and evidence on the potential of precise control possible through electromyography is encouraging.

Workers at Queen's University in Kingston, Ontario, in Canada have been able to elicit a response not from just a particular bundle of nerve fibers, as the Russians do in their artificial hand, but from an individual "motor unit" amongst the thousands. John V. Basmajian at Queen's inserts a fine wire electrode into a small muscle at the base of a subject's thumb and connects the electrode to two oscilloscopes, a loudspeaker and a tape recorder. By watching the oscilloscopes and listening to the popping sounds muscular activity makes in the loudspeaker, the subject learns to completely relax the muscle in question, and then to actuate single motor units in the muscle bundle, a feat impossible without feedback not normally associated with muscular activity. Some subjects were able to summon up responses of individual and coded nerves, as many as five. Further training led to the production of a "galloping" rhythm in the loudspeaker, and drumbeats on order! Coupling of such signals to some artificial device could lead to a delicacy of control to make the Russian prosthesis resemble an old-fashioned hook.

A greater refinement of the muscle training technique has recently been reported by Dr. John Lyman and his associates at UCLA. Feeling that the oscilloscope training method was not ideal, particularly with a naive subject, and that the loudspeaker method left similar shortcomings, the researchers devised a visual display board showing the schematic diagram of a man. Lights placed at appropriate muscle sites lit up when the proper muscle action was made by the subject. Performance of subjects seemed to bear out the theory back of the new training method. At the beginning of the training, no desired response could be made by an amputee subject. At the final training period, involving 101 cycles of muscular activity, scores ranging from 97 percent to 100 percent were recorded for the various muscles involved. And it was demonstrated that contractions of desired muscles could be made at the rate of one per second.

Wolfe's novel, *Limbo*, describes the training of athletes fitted with "pros" of a type much like the Russian artificial hand. These men learn a delicate control impossible to people with natural limbs, strangely reminiscent of present-day experiments in refining elicited muscle responses. *Limbo* was written in 1952, several years before actual work was begun on myoelectric exploitation, but with an eye on Norbert Wiener's predictions for cybernetics.

"*All right, fellows.*" It was Theo's voice. "*That's enough horsing around. Let's do some dexterities and discernments.*"

It was easy to follow the vaulting bodies, as they rose and fell the tubes in their limbs blinked agitated semaphores; the clearing looked like an enormous telephone switchboard gone berserk. And there was more illumination than that. The amps seemed to be carrying powerful searchlights—no, Martine saw now that the index finger of each amp's right hand was itself a searchlight, from its tip projected a beam of light.

"*Come on, you guys,*" Theo said. "*This isn't getting us anywhere. Your jumping's fine—it's your d-and-d's that are ragged—*"

Shouts of protest from the playful athletes: "*Follow the leader! Let's play follow the leader!*"

The last suggestion seemed to appeal to everybody. "*Great idea!*" "*Follow the leader!*" "*Come on, Theo, you be leader!*" *A dozen index fingers pointed at Theo, his bulging-skulled head was bathed in light.*

"*All right, men,*" he said humorously. "*All right. This is no way for humanists to pass the time, but I guess you deserve a little relaxation.*"

The beams of light were still on him. He bent his legs. "*Here goes!*" *he called, and took off from the ground. Up he rocketed, thirty feet or more, caught hold of a raffia branch and whirled around it, the tubes in his limbs leaving trails like miniature comets. Then he let go and dropped, his body twisting so fast that it could be seen only as a twinkling blur. There were whistles, shouts of approval.*

Now the athletes followed suit: one by one they jumped, pinwheeled, spun back to earth.

Theo laughed. "*What a bunch of duds!*" *he said.* "*Not one of you made it. Haven't you noticed anything about my sweat shirt?*"

The lights flashed on him again. He turned around slowly, the young men gasped in surprise: the "*M*" *that had been on his chest was now on his back.*

"*Let that be a lesson to you,*" he said. "*That shows you what you can do when you really concentrate on your dexterities—as I was dropping from the tree I slipped my arms out of my sleeves, twisted my shirt around, and put it on again backwards. You'd better do some woodshedding on your discernments too—if you'd been a little more discerning you would have noticed it. . . ."*

Researchers have not yet achieved the virtuosity of *Limbo's* artificial limb makers, but progress of a modest sort is being made. At Cleveland's Case Institute of Technology a three-year, forty-man project funded by the Department of Health, Education, and Welfare has resulted in a computer-controlled myoelectric hand.

Instead of the atomic power used in the fictional limbs, the Case device is actuated by carbon dioxide gas at a pressure of 600 pounds per square inch. Myoelectric signals from the trapezius muscle in the shoulder are amplified and fed to a stimulator situated over paralyzed muscles of the subject's lower arm. This stimulation makes it possible for him to open and close his hand. The gas-powered splint that moves the whole arm is computer-controlled, with the program initiated and halted by eyelid movements! An override system consists of an infrared light source in the wearer's spectacles, beamed as needed toward photocells on the arm splint.

This prototype artificial hand is too expensive for anything except use as a research tool but it is hoped that it will lead to a practical, moderately priced replacement for handicapped people.

Biopower

Thus far we have talked of using electrical signals generated in the living body for *controlling* electronic equipment. Such signals are at best of the order of a few thousandths of a volt and obviously do not represent very much power generated. To use them even for control signals necessitates amplifying them many thousandfold. In light of this it may seem fantastic to investigate the living body for sources of electric *power*. But then, the whole idea of the cyborg is fantastic.

Familiar with electricity from early childhood, we come to take it much for granted. Electricity powers our homes, some of our transportation, and much industry. It comes out of the wall socket, or from storage batteries. There is a new device being developed into a practical power source—the fuel cell, a sort of battery with a gas tank. Most living things, from bacteria upwards, are fuel cells of a special kind—biochemical fuel cells.

Oxidation of a fuel, such as the burning of wood in the presence of air, produces energy in the form of heat. A chemical battery oxidizes a fuel, but suppresses the heat production and produces a flow of electrons instead. Part of the food we eat is turned into electricity inside our bodies, as we have seen in considering brain waves, myoelectric nerve signals and so on. A new branch of biological science now is investigating the phenomenon of "biopower," the production of appreciable quantities of electricity in living things.

Fifty years ago a biologist named Potter put together a number of yeast "cells" to make a biobattery with an output of a tiny fraction of a watt. He discovered that his living cells had a voltage of about half a volt. For half a century this remained an interesting laboratory curiosity. Then in the late 1950's a number of researchers picked up the ball and began to run in all directions. As a result the Navy developed "marine biocells," in which microorganisms obligingly converted marine matter into modest amounts of electricity to power small pieces of electronic equipment needed on buoys and other floating gear.

Another group demonstrated a radio powered by a test tube full of sea water and bacteria, and operated a model boat on a similar biocell taking its fuel from the water. There was the standard amount of loose talk of converting the Black Sea into a huge biobattery to bring a kind of TVA to underprivileged Asiatics who had never before known the blessings of electric power.

There are more achievable uses for biopower, particularly in closed-cycle systems for spaceships where living organisms could function to produce power, purify water and air, and even grow food! This in itself is surprising enough, but the biopower people have much more to demonstrate. Scientists at General Electric's Space Sciences Laboratory in Pennsylvania moved from bacteria to a more advanced form of life in the search for bioelectricity. Working with rats, they found that appreciable amounts of power were generated in the muscles of these animals. At a symposium in 1962, J. J. Konikoff and L. W. Reynolds reported on their progress.

They called their work "bioelectrogenesis," the generation of electricity in living matter. Part of their research concerned yeast cells such as Potter had pioneered in 1911. But they also investigated the production of bioelectricity in rats. After anesthetizing the subjects, they attached electrodes of platinum black to the coelom and the skin of the brachial region. The rodent power plant produced 300 microamperes of current at 3/10 of a volt. A flashlight cell produces far more current, of course, but only about 1½ volts.

Given this new power supply, General Electric researchers built a small oscillator operating at 500 kilocycles and designed for the low voltage available. This was operated successfully by the rat power supply for periods up to eight hours.

There are a number of ways of generating electricity, even in living things. One is by connecting electrodes to sites in the body at different galvanic levels, as was done with General Electric's rat. Another is to implant a cylindrical platinum electrode in a vessel, such as the cecum passing intestinal fluid. This would be a fuel cell in the sense of an artificial type, except that it is implanted in a living thing and uses organic "fuel," generating current from fluid passed through the ring electrode.

In addition to the task of operating an implanted electronic pacemaker, bioelectricity might also power a transmitter like G.E.'s "rat radio" to telemeter information to remote stations. There are two important phases of this work. In laboratory research it is helpful to know what is going on inside the body of the subject. If this could be done without the nuisance and technical disadvantages of wires, it would be most helpful and accurate. Scientists also like to know what is happening to experimental subjects at a distance, whether they be wild geese whose mating instincts are being studied, or astronauts under the stress of space flight.

Something approaching this was announced by the Veterans Administration in Boston in May, 1964. Dr. Irving R. Levine described the system in which a patient living in Braintree, some twenty miles from the VA center, was monitored and treated by remote control. Signals from a bioelectric amplifier attached to the patient, suffering from a neurospastic disorder, were relayed to the VA by telephone company Dataphone equipment. The system is called Telemedography.

An implanted transmitter, powered by bioelectricity, could automatically send information to a central receiver on the condition and whereabouts of wild life and astronauts, as well as medical outpatients on whom the doctor wishes to keep tab. Exercising the imagination a bit, the scheme could work in reverse, and radio a signal back to the subject to adjust his pacemaker as needed, signal a wandering duck to come home, or tell a space traveler that he was dangerously near the end of his endurance.

Articles have appeared in the popular press that extended General Electric's bioelectrogenesis studies to fantastic extremes: Electrodes from a battery in the body producing electricity from muscle, blood or whatever, are led to a plug-in socket in the wrist, or head or other handy location so that the wired individual could plug in his personal electric fan, hearing aid, transistor radio or even Dick Tracy's new wrist television! Tape recorders, television cameras for spies and radar sets for the blind are envisioned by wide-eyed reporters who also foresee the day man recharges his biobatteries by plugging himself into a socket!

The human heart is a powerful mechanism. Where the rat-powered radio operated on 90 *micro*watts of power, the heart requires a motor of about 35 watts or 1/30 horsepower to replace it.

This makes it about 400,000 times as powerful as the rat battery. This power source potential is behind the idea of using muscles to generate electricity via the piezoelectric method. This scheme, mentioned earlier and used by one research team to power a pacemaker in a dog, converts pressure into electrical current.

The future of bioelectrical power is intriguing. The Navy envisions schemes for operating weapons remotely and with no time lag as is common with conventional firing techniques. There are already experimental weapons systems in which the soldier merely looks toward his target and flicks his eyes to fire the gun. This seemingly sophisticated concept is crude by contrast with the newer myoelectric method of doing something by merely "thinking about it."

This possibility, and the need from which it stems, were accurately foreseen by Bernal in 1929 when he wrote, "On the motor side we shall soon be obliged to control mechanisms for which two hands and feet are inadequate. *Volition* would simplify its operation." (The italics are mine.)

Because of parallels between the body's control system and the technology of electronics, which parallels are surely more than fortuitous, by the way, the cyborg seems sure to be increasingly electrical and electronic in nature. Engineers will exploit human nervous systems more and more in a fashion similar to the juggling performed on artificial circuits to achieve desired results.

Bernal also wrote, "We badly need a small sense organ for detecting wireless frequencies, infra-red, ultra-violet, and X-rays, ears for supersonics, temperature detectors, electrical detectors, and chemical organs. We may train a number of hot and cold and pain receptors to take over." No one yet has "X-ray eyes" but achievements are in the offing that seem a prelude to just this sort of creation of new sensors.

9 *Drugs*

"It is well," replied my visitor. "Lanyon, you remember your vows: what follows is under the seal of our profession. And now, you who have so long been bound to the most narrow and material views, you who have derided your superiors—behold!"

He put the glass to his lips and drank at one gulp. A cry followed; he reeled, staggered, clutched at the table and held on, staring with injected eyes, gasping with open mouth; and as I looked there came, I thought, a change—he seemed to swell—his face became suddenly black and the features seemed to melt and alter—and the next moment, I had sprung to my feet and leaped back against the wall, my arm raised to shield me from that prodigy, my mind submerged in terror.

"O God!" I screamed, and "O God!" again and again; for there before my eyes—pale and shaken, and half fainting, and groping before him with his hands, like a man restored from death—there stood Henry Jekyll!

Robert Louis Stevenson
The Strange Case of Dr. Jekyll and Mr. Hyde
1886

Just as there are a number of ways to skin a cat, so are there more ways to change man than to fit him with artificial organs, radar eyes or atom-powered legs. Natural man may be *chemically* altered to effect profound changes. The dramatic success of drugs like cortisone, ACTH and others is an example of an artificial take-over of glandular functions. If the liver or thyroid is not doing its job, it is sometimes possible to provide the body otherwise with the extracts these organs should produce. Diabetics are permitted near-normal lives through rigidly controlled diet and doses of insulin in carefully measured and adjusted amounts to keep the blood sugar level close to normal. Drugs, then, can be considered cyborg agents just as legitimate as spectacles and wooden legs. They are not as obvious, but are often dramatic and far-reaching in the changes they make on the body, which after all depends on chemistry at least as much as physics.

Early drugs and their misuse stemmed directly from the belief in magic. Included in primitive pharmacopoeia were such varied substances as "potable gold," pearls, crocodile dung, powdered mummy, unicorn's horn, and sarsaparilla. Gold and pearls were obviously expensive drugs, but unicorn's horn too was costly. A specimen in Dresden was estimated as worth $75,000, a fortune in the sixteenth century. A French king refused to part with his horn for $100,000, a rare tribute indeed to a mythical animal!

The first edition of the Encyclopaedia Britannica described the curative powers of the drug "usnea." Usnea was a substance scraped from the skull of a criminal who had been hung in chains. Cotton Mather used crushed sow bugs in his practice, and scientist Robert Boyle included in his revised list of drugs the sole of an old shoe "worn by some man that walked much." Horse dung mixed with white wine was prescribed for Cardinal Richelieu on his deathbed, and French dentists recommended the patient's own urine as an effective mouthwash in cases of toothache.

Early drugs included spices, and Columbus opened up the new world in his attempt to find new trade routes for the drug commerce. Later colonists to New England would be accused of making and selling fake nutmegs of wood for the treatment of disease. England's Charles II was a classic victim of the drug practitioner, dosed with antimony, rock salt, bitters, mallow leaves, violets, camomile, fennel, linseed, cinnamon, cardamon, saffron, cochineal, aloes, sneezing powder, cowslip, barley water, licorice, almonds, wine, absinthe, anise, thistle leaves, mint, rue, angelica, melon seeds, manna, slippery elm, black cherry water, flowers of lime, lily of the valley, peony, lavender, dissolved pearls, gentian root, nutmeg, quinine, cloves and forty drops of extract of human skull! Then "so as not to appear to fail in doing their duty in any detail," they brought into play the most active cordial. This *coup de grâce* was a mixture of "Raleigh's antidote," pearl julep, and ammonia. The patient, unfortunately, died.

The physician Galen developed a therapeutic theory based on several thousand drugs, many of them herbs. The expression "cool as a cucumber" is said to spring from this early drug approach. It persists today in sassafras tea "to cool the blood" and preparations like Lydia Pinkham's for female complaints.

Ineffective as most preparations were for curing diseases or working as love potions, the potency of drugs was known early. Chemicals could kill quickly, spirituous liquors affected mind and body strongly, and narcotics were known as pain killers and hallucination producers. Wholesale insanity was caused, apparently, by tainted rye. The first scientific uses of drugs were quite probably as anesthetics, and a new era of medicine began, leading to today's "pep" pills, tranquilizers, contraceptives, and so on.

The Mind Changers

Most drug applications are intended to bring man back to an approximation of what nature intended for him. Drugs may also be used to produce a result not usually found in nature, to cause secondary evolution of a sort. It is normal for man to sleep about eight hours a day, despite the few who seem to get by on a fraction of that. If we create, through drugs or otherwise, a man who requires only one hour of sleep in twenty-four or who sleeps all but one of those hours, we will have produced a different creature. The use of sleeping pills carried to rash extremes causes permanent sleep. However, it is possible to medicate the body so that it will remain in a somnolent state all or nearly all the time.

Going in the other direction, many humans, from cramming college students to long-distance solo fliers, have extended the period of sleeplessness from the normal 16 hours to several times that with pep pills or more scientific stimulation. One long-distance flier reportedly remained awake from 24 hours prior to a 48-hour flight over water until 48 hours after landing. An airline pilot with a scientific turn of mind, he prepared himself by practicing with drugs before the flight. "Psychic energizers" had the effect of reducing fatigue and enabling him to concentrate more intently on the problems at hand. Forthcoming flights in space will give ample opportunity for more of this sort of unnatural wakefulness, and also for long periods of sleep on extended flights of a boring nature.

There are other ways man alters himself with drugs. Many travelers are indebted to Dramamine and other preparations that adjust their balance center to block nausea and vertigo. This is again mere compensation in an attempt to regain normal powers or tolerance to environment. But the principle can be extended to produce a man with powers beyond the natural, and who can function efficiently in a different environment.

Fish is a legendary brain food. How efficacious such a diet actually is is problematical and may parallel the old wives' tale about eggs being a stimulus for the reproductive organs. Surely neither hurts its respective cause.

More scientific are the results obtained in careful experiments. The use of "truth serums" and the technique of narcosynthesis in efforts to recall memories from deep in the brain's nooks and crannies appear to be partly successful. Much of this may be simply the overriding of nature's inhibitory system. Some claim that memory is natural; only forgetting takes conscious effort. We forget what is unpleasant to remember, or what we do not choose to retain in our conscious minds for other reasons. With drugs and hypnosis, it seems possible to reach past this barrier and probe information stored in the unconscious part of the brain.

The Hallucinogens

For centuries men have been aware of the weird effects certain drugs have on the mind. Hallucination produced by a virus in rye drove whole villages out of their minds and killed many of them. This substance was ergot. Lesser agents were not so potent and belladonna, henbane, and marijuana are familiar around the world for inducing euphoria and other states.

The soma of Huxley's *Brave New World* was based on such a drug used in India. In the New World, the real one, the Aztecs reportedly used buttons of the peyote cactus to make Montezuma's coronation seem even grander. Such use persists today, and is part of the religion of the American Indians in the southwest. These people number some quarter of a million, and the courts have permitted use of the drug in this connection.

Empirical use of natural hallucinogens has long been effective but scientists have recently succeeded in greatly improving on them in the laboratory. From peyote, for example, comes the much stronger mescaline (from the Mescalero Apaches, who are users). Mexican mushrooms yield psilocybin and psilocin. And from ergot, the rye mould, comes LSD–25, or d-lysergic acid. Mescaline is the weakest of the four drugs. Psilocybin is about 100 times stronger, and LSD another 70 times as potent! In Huxley's book the soma dose was described as "Half a gram is better than a damn!" But only a few millionths of an ounce of LSD–25 sends the user into hours of weird psychical fantasies and sometimes revelations concerning esthetics, comprehension of his fellow man, the universe and even God. The hallucinatory effects also include sight, sound, smell and taste phenomena.

Research has disclosed a similarity between hallucinogenic drugs and the adrenal hormone epinephrine. Since the brain is an electrochemically stimulated organ such "neurohormones" play a part in transmission of impulses between neurons. Perhaps drugs may be valuable in correcting or alleviating mental disorders such as schizophrenia. There are other more intriguing possibilities.

It might seem that mind-changing drugs would produce effects like the life-of-the-party drunk who only thinks he is so terrific. However, art work done by some subjects using LSD–25 and other drugs indicates stimulation of creativity. With the removal of inhibitions there are also hints of greater insight, perception and comprehension.

Psychologists at Harvard experimenting in this direction with hallucinogens ran afoul of authorities of that institution and were dropped from the faculty. They have continued on their own and talk hopefully of "transcendental living," "expanded conscious-ness" and even "experiential typewriters" that will record the sen-sory fantasies produced by their pharmacopoeia.

There are also those in the military who are interested in the hallucinating drugs and inevitably there is talk of "brainwashing" in a literal sense, with potent drugs introduced into water sup-plies to convert whole populations into blissful idiots while their conquerors take over without the need for physical force.

All these fantastic claims have a basis in sound fact—that the brain depends in part upon chemistry to function. Just as vitamins put roses in our cheeks and help us to see better, so might other substances make our mental capacity flourish.

An Australian researcher named S. Rose tackled the problem of long-term continuous injections of drugs into animals and devel-oped what is called the "Rose osmotic injector." This inoculator, attached to a test animal such as a mouse, continuously and auto-matically provides the correct amount of medication into the sys-term through the means of osmotic pressure. In principle it is similar to the more elaborate artificial pancreas developed by Dr. Kolff and mentioned in the chapter on artificial internal organs. The hypodermic needle might be considered a stopgap substitute organ.

Man's breathing has a certain, fairly fixed rate, as does his blood pressure and pulse rate. These things occur unconsciously, under control of the autonomic nervous system. The Rose method of injecting the needed drug is similar, in that there is no conscious effort on the part of the subject. A human cyborg, augmented by drugs, might be thus automatically medicated to make him more effective.

Originally tried on rats, the Rose device was later implanted in larger animals and functioned entirely automatically. A man so equipped with an automatic Miltown dispenser would be a changed individual, not capable of forgetting to take his pills and thus reverting to normalcy or whatever his condition without medication.

How much change can be effected in the human physiology by drugs is not certain. Surely there will be no quick-change results as in the story of Jekyll and Hyde. In this fictional treatment of the idea, complete and rapid reversal was accomplished in both directions until the process at last became almost irreversible. Narcotics users have such a terrible time "kicking the habit" because changes are made in the cells themselves. Morphine has the effect of making the cell depend on it for normal life. When it is withheld, cells sicken and can even die, but when morphine treatment is restored the cell quickly improves.

Genetic Effects

The recent episode involving the German drug Thalidomide was a tragic example of irreversibility. Produced as a sleeping pill or tranquilizer, this preparation was taken by the millions of tablets each month in Germany and in appreciable amounts in England and elsewhere. What the women who enjoyed their benefits could not know was that the tablets were wreaking havoc on the unborn babies they carried and because of whom, ironically, they may have felt the need for the drug in the first place. The result was some 5,000 "Thalidomide babies," horrible examples of the tampering it is possible for man to do with chemicals.

Thalidomide affected the fetus apparently only during a limited portion of pregnancy, according to analyses of 120 cases. Pills taken on the thirty-fifth day after the woman's last menstrual period resulted in the absence of ears in the infant. Taken during the thirty-eighth to fifty-second days, Thalidomide caused "phocomelia," the seal-flipper deformity in which only tiny hands appeared and these right at the shoulder. From the thirty-ninth to forty-first days within this period, complete absence of arms was caused. Between the forty-first and forty-fourth days the penalty was complete absence of legs. Finally, if taken first on the fifty-fifth day, there seemed to be no harmful effect on the fetus, although of course women have been warned not to take the drug at any time during pregnancy.

It was known that exposure to German measles could cause women to have children with blinding cataracts. This was discovered in an epidemic of such cases in Australia in 1940, the same year researchers noted that rats from whom Vitamin B-2 had been withheld bore deformed offspring. But here was the first known example of an artificially given chemical producing a different kind of human being.

Although some facts in the Thalidomide tragedy are puzzling, and some think that other factors may have been involved also, much evidence points directly to the drug as having affected the cells in the budding limbs of the babies and preventing their development as nature had scheduled. Because of the tragedy, paradoxically, science is learning things about the development of a baby that may throw light on such abnormalities, which occurred long before there was a drug like Thalidomide. Knowing the chemical structure of the drug and the effects it has, perhaps a counter drug might be produced to prevent these deformities arising from heredity or congenital causes. Another possibility considered is that of intentional chemical alteration of life while it is developing in the womb.

Thalidomide resulted in the death of some 2,500 youngsters, half of those affected by the drug. Other drugs, designed to prevent conception, prevent the birth of *uncounted* numbers of children. Here we run headlong into questions of mores and morals, of ethics and theology, of ecology and cosmology. We will discuss this aspect of artificial man more fully in a later chapter, but it is worthy of note here in connection with other aspects of the effect of drugs on the human mind and body in producing unnatural results.

The extremes of the cyborg range from adding mechanical appliances to what nature has provided, to "gene-tinkering" to produce wanted varieties of men. Thalidomide produced a variant somewhere between these two methods, more fundamental than the mechanical change after birth, yet not so basic as a priori rearrangement of genes and chromosomes would be.

Radiation Protection

A hazard of a very serious kind is radiation. Natural radiation has been bombarding man for ages, and it is the impinging of cosmic rays on his cells that gives rise to the "sports," or mutations, that occur from time to time. Such mutations are the basis for genetic evolution and as such are very important. Man's contribution to atomic radiation may have similar genetic repercussions; it is perhaps too early to tell. However, it is known that other effects occur here and now, without any wait for future generations. Hiroshima, Nagasaki, and lesser nuclear catastrophes are tragic proof of that.

In time, although not in our time, nature will undoubtedly evolve men impervious to atomic radiation if they are continually subjected to it. Meanwhile, man himself is working on the problem of creating a new kind of man who will be protected against radiation. One method is to add an outer skin to a human; a skin of lead several feet thick. This results in a rather cumbersome being, and a more efficacious method is indicated. A possible chemical approach has been investigated at the School of Aviation Medicine at the Brooks Air Force Base in Texas.

Dr. Walter H. Whitcomb of the Radiobiology Branch reports that treating monkeys with the drugs cysteine and aminoethylisothioronium increased their resistance to radiation. This line of research will surely be pursued in an effort to develop protection not only for monkeys and men exposed to the radiation dangers in space, but also those of us who stay at home in an atmosphere of radioactive fallout.

The potion that instantly changed Stevenson's Jekyll into a depraved Hyde has not been brewed as yet, although commonplace preparations accomplish something of the sort over a slightly longer period of time. More important are other uses of drugs in the alteration of man. Chemicals can put on and take off weight for users. They kill pain, induce sleep or wakefulness, calm us down or pep us up.

Chemicals, once derisively described as "internal amulets," and with good reason, now can affect the immune reaction in grafting operations, cause hibernation, increase our tolerance of heat and other radiation. Perhaps most importantly, drugs can drastically alter our genetic structure or at least its operation. Some researchers on aging look to chemicals as a possible slower of the process. A prominent cyborg technician then is he who hopefully tampers with man's chemistry, searching for an elixir of life that is really what its name implies.

10 *Hypothermia*

INEVITABILITY OF A FREEZER PROGRAM

It is easy to perceive that a large-scale freezer program must inexorably develop, sooner or later, whether or not my degree of optimism becomes general, and whether or not my personal efforts exert much influence.

We recall that suspended animation of humans (by freezing alive, without serious freezing damage, so that the subject can be thawed out and restored to active life at any time) is generally agreed to be in the cards. So far as I know, not a single expert doubts that this will come about, although there are wide differences of opinion as to when the technique will be mastered. Estimates vary from about five years on up; my general impression is that a consensus might point to success within the life-times of a majority of people now living.

As soon as suspended animation is practicable, persons with incurable diseases will surely be frozen alive to await the time that cures are discovered. It can scarcely be doubted that this development, at the very least and latest, would provide the entering wedge for the freezer program.

Robert C. W. Ettinger
The Prospect of Immortality
Doubleday, 1964.

Quite suddenly, the notion of a kind of immortality based on suspended animation via the freezer technique has gained new popularity. Long a favorite of the writer of science fiction, the basic idea of stopping—or at least slowing—life seems sound. What kept it fictional was lack of supporting technology. About the time of the various technological revolutions of the World War II era a new field called "cryogenics" flourished, and one needed technology for suspended animation was at hand.

Immortal man would be superman indeed, and so "hypothermia" is an important part of the cyborg idea. Not yet in Webster's dictionary, but surely destined for such currency, hypothermia is defined in McGraw-Hill's Encyclopedia of Science and Technology as "a state of living organisms characterized by decreases in deep body temperature and associated changes in behavior and internal body processes." More simply put, hypothermia is that state in which temperature of the body is reduced sufficiently to slow the processes of life. Hibernating animals are in hypothermia.

Not everyone shares the optimism of Robert Ettinger, author of *The Prospect of Immortality*, of course, but biologist Jean Rostand of the French Academy wrote an enthusiastic preface, concluding with the statement that the book deserves to be read and thought about.

Life and Heat

Occasionally we read of a person who has almost frozen, and yet made a remarkable recovery. Recently a woman was brought to a Tulsa hospital after having lain outdoors all night in street clothes in freezing weather. Estimated body temperature was lower than 60 degrees F., compared with a normal reading of a little above 98 F. Warmed with special blankets and a "hypogastric balloon," she recovered.

As in many such cases, this patient reportedly was under the influence of alcohol. According to doctors this fact, paradoxically, contributed to saving her life. The body in hypothermia, or very low temperature, uses only a small part of the normal oxygen requirement. All the body's living processes slow and thus less heat is required to sustain what life is left.

Life is synonymous with heat. Without heat there can be no life. When metals are cooled sufficiently, all molecular motion ceases, so that in cryogenic circuits there is no resistance to currents of electricity. When living things are cooled the same sort of thing happens. Cells slow their rate of living and finally stop the process altogether. But if everything stops, what happens to such things as memory? Strangely, freezing experiments with animals indicate that memory is retained even after prolonged freezing and complete cessation of "life." This is in contrast to the theory that continuous activity in the brain is necessary to the retention of memory.

Animals have a built-in thermostat that normally maintains body temperature within a very narrow range. For example, a fever of a few degrees in man can prove fatal if prolonged. The body maintains this internal temperature despite great extremes in outside environment. In hot weather we perspire and thus cool ourselves. In cold weather other animals are protected by fur, man by his clothing or furnaces. Shivering is another device for generating additional heat when needed.

When all methods fail, the body temperature drops. Another cause of body cooling is failure of the temperature-regulating mechanism in the hypothalamus. Finally, hypothermia may be induced by drugs.

Background for Hypothermia

Hypothermia is nothing new. We are familiar with it to some extent in the hibernation of animals. At lowered temperatures, their bodies slow their metabolism and subsist on stored-up food. Fish live in water just above the freezing point. Henry Power froze and thawed vinegar eels three hundred years ago and attempts to similarly cool the human body reportedly extend back that far. In 1796 Dr. John Hunter in England conducted some more or less scientific experiments that he thought would lead to suspended animation in animals and humans and thus prolong life appreciably. Unfortunately for the fish Hunter experimented with, they died. This was perhaps a blessing in disguise as far as potential human subjects of Hunter's were concerned, however.

Dr. Alexis Carrel was among the many scientists who subsequently considered the idea of suspended animation with interest. In *Man the Unknown* his judgment is not optimistic:

> *Basal metabolism is remarkably constant. The organism maintains the normal activity of its chemical exchanges under the most adverse conditions. Exposure to intense cold does not decrease the rhythm of nutrition. The temperature of the body falls only on the approach of death. On the contrary, bears and raccoons lower their metabolism in winter, and fall into a state of slower life. Certain arthopodous animals, Tardigrada, completely stop their metabolism when they are dried. A condition of latent life is thus induced. After a lapse of several weeks, if one moistens these desiccated animals, they revive, and the rhythm of their life again becomes normal.*
>
> *It might be possible perhaps, to prolong life, cure certain diseases, and give higher opportunities to exceptionally gifted individuals, if human beings could be made to hibernate from time to time. But we are not capable of decreasing the rate of metabolism, except by the barbarous method that consists of removing the thyroid gland. And even that method is quite insufficient. As far as man is concerned, latent life, for the moment, is an impossible form of existence.*

New Techniques

In theory it is easy to suspend animation. At absolute zero all molecular motion ceases; life comes to a halt. In practice it is not necessary to reach such a low temperature; life seems to be suspended far above absolute zero. Unfortunately it is not only suspended but usually destroyed too. Since living cells are made up largely of water, which expands on freezing, all sorts of physical havoc is wrought as the temperature of living things drops. Chemical changes take place too as water freezes out of solutions, leaving a higher proportion of salt or other elements. So brutally freezing a living thing is not generally a guarantee of life remaining on subsequent thawing.

New methods and equipment permit faster freezing. Such a technique was adopted by the frozen food industry, and better results obtained through smaller crystals of ice formed during the freezing process. No crystals at all, a glassy frozen product described as "vitrefied," is the dream or philosophers' stone of the cryobiologist. The compound glycerol was a fair try at this cryogenic catalyst.

As sometimes happens, the happy accident of serendipity greatly advanced the state of the cryobiology art. At the National Institute for Medical Research in London, researchers Polge, Smith, and Parkes were attempting to freeze fowl spermatozoa in a solution of levulose. Levulose is honey sugar, and a bottle of this was accidentally interchanged with one containing 10 percent glycerol and 1 percent albumen. Amazingly the spermatozoa survived cooling to −79 C. (dry-ice temperature) and subsequent thawing. A follow-up test with levulose failed, and in investigating the mystery, researchers discovered the mistake involving glycerol and cryobiology gained a potent tool. This was in 1948. Rostand had achieved similar results in 1946, but not at such low temperatures.

For more immediate applications, freezing techniques keep the contents of banks of human spare parts usable for long periods of time. Corneas, skin, and other tissues including blood and endocrine tissue are successfully preserved by freezing. The long-range goal is to keep an entire human in the deep freeze for a variety of reasons. As might be expected, there are some problems connected with this idea.

Medical Uses

Hypothermia has long been used experimentally in the laboratory. Animals have been cooled as low as −32 F. and revived successfully after more than an hour at this temperature. The Russians have done laboratory work on freezing bats and restoring them to life. British scientists have done remarkable work on hamsters, galagos and mice.

Hypothermia is important to the medical profession far beyond its use as an interesting experimental technique, and is part of the relatively new field of cryobiology. Surgery on the heart and brain would be far easier if it could be accomplished without blood circulation. At normal temperatures, withholding oxygen (via the blood) from the brain for more than a few minutes is crippling or fatal. Obviously the heart cannot be stopped for that length of time either, unless provision is made for routing the bypassed blood through a heart-lung machine in the interim. But if the body is cooled down to about 86 F., the need for oxygen is also reduced, and heart and brain operations can be performed almost bloodlessly, with operating times as long as forty-five minutes instead of three or four.

Hypothermia is also of benefit in transplant operations, since the delay in regaining normal temperature apparently gives the new organ a chance to get used to its new surroundings in a more leisurely manner.

Old body-cooling techniques worked from the outside in. Patients were immersed in a tub of ice, a painful process that required sedation or other means of alleviating pain. More recently the technique of refrigerating the blood itself in a cooling device outside the body has proved far more effective. Hypothermia is "deep body cooling," and the blood quickly gets to the nooks and crannies that take a long time to lose heat by normal conduction.

With new methods, the icy dreams of Dr. Hunter and other visionaries who foresaw suspended animation seem more possible. In the deep freeze, we may choose to file ourselves away for the terrestrial future, or make space voyages of a hundred or even a thousand years. Another factor in space travel makes hypothermia for such uses more attractive. The hibernating animal gets by on a minimum of food; a hibernating space man could do the same and save much precious weight. Hypothermia on earth requires elaborate equipment since the environment is normally much warmer than the required temperatures.

Freezing can preserve; it can also kill effectively. This result, unwanted in many processes, led to the development of a hypothermia technique called cryosurgery. Using hollow-pointed probes, cooled by liquid nitrogen, surgeons destroy diseased tissue, repair retinal detachments, and do other delicate surgical operations.

Immortality

The use of hypothermia as a medical tool for "bloodless" surgery, for killing diseased cells and for other beneficial purposes in hospital and laboratory seems mild when compared with the idea suggested in Ettinger's book on immortality. We have discussed the exploitation of cryobiology in preserving sperm, blood, and other tissue; and such techniques are expected to make possible whole-organ preservation before long. Preservation of the whole body is seemingly a logical ultimate outcome of such work—the suspended animation of a human body for periods of years for resuscitation at some later time.

Jean Rostand in his preface to Ettinger's book cites a story by the Frenchman Edmond About entitled "The Man with the Broken Ear," published in 1861. In it a scientist "dries out" one of Napoleon's soldiers frozen to "death" in Russia and suspends his life for several decades, at which time he revives the patient with only the minor damage implied in the title. We have seen that even a hundred years ago such an idea was not new. Our own Benjamin Franklin wished he could be resurrected in a century to see how things were coming along.

The idea has wondrous possibilities. A twenty-year-old person might exchange his remaining fifty or so years for periodic peeks at the next five thousand years, via the deep-freeze route. But Ettinger adds more of an incentive. Medical science is even now on the verge of finding cures for many ailments, learning how to transplant organs and to build artificial ones, and possibly halt the process of aging or at least slow it somewhat. Why, asks Ettinger, cheat those who will not live until that happy day of its benefits? Why not instead freeze each of us at "death" and preserve the corpse until such time as it can be thawed out and cured?

The chaos such a prospect threatens those institutions like funeral parlors, insurance companies, banks, the law, citizenship, and so on is blithely pointed out but mostly turned to advantage. Everyone who could scrape up the price of freezing and cold storage for himself plus a small deposit in the bank would awaken centuries from now with the prospect of rejuvenation and millions of dollars to spend, an annuity built on compound interest while he slept in the vault!

There would be some sticky problems, such as that of the status of marital partners whose widows or widowers had remarried in the "first life." Storage space for the bodies frozen and stacked like cordwood might be hard to come by, although Ettinger points out that a cube-shaped freezer 30 meters on a side would hold 18,000 bodies. Also, he feels that there is room on the planet for some 40 billion humans, so we have some way to go from the present population of 3½ billion.

Those who could not afford their own freezers would of course go to a "potter's freezer." The Communists might have an edge on us with regard to low-cost freezing, since bodies could be stored in Siberian pits, insulated with cheap straw and cooled with dry ice, rather than the expensive liquid helium we capitalists would require.

In his conclusion to the book, Ettinger suggests that 1964 may be the dawn of the freezer-centered era; that before the end of that year the first frozen human asset may be laid away with his cold storage rent paid, a modest sum in the bank, and his vital statistics tucked away in the memory of a computer against the day of his second coming. Not so, and only a few are so optimistic and none so publicly as Mr. Ettinger. Most involved scientists take a more guarded view, some of them poking fun at the idea of frozen man.

At the 1963 meeting of the American Society for Artificial Internal Organs, Dr. E. Converse Peirce II devoted his presidential address principally to the subject of hypothermia, much of it in light vein. The sun, he predicted, would be dead within seven billion years. At that time the earth would be so cold that life would have to exist at very low temperatures, and since this was inevitable, he suggested that we accept hypothermia, relax and enjoy it.

He pointed out that coincident with the society's first meeting in 1955, cartoonist Al Capp was covering the subject of hypothermia in his comic strip "Lil Abner." General Bullmoose preferred to sleep in a deep freeze and wake up several hours later "not one second older!" Peirce said that it would be marvelous when the deep freeze was available as a baby sitter, and for long space travels. Enough suitable refrigerator units might even postpone the necessity of facing the problems of the population explosion, since:

> *The freezer's a fine and private place*
> *And none I think do there embrace.*

Along with his levity, he pointed out the many uses of the freezing technique and means of achieving that state at which the "cost of living" was so low.

Hypothermia lends itself admirably to the making of jokes. To be expected are comic allusions to "cold, cold world," "cold heart," and "cooling it" in the "dormantories" suggested by Ettinger. All of which mirth will not change the fact that hypothermia has come of age. There are already those who owe their lives to the technique as used in heart or brain surgery. Many others have benefited from blood, bone, nerves, corneas, and other tissues preserved by freezing. Including perhaps frozen sperm.

The remainder of the journey to the apparent promise of hypothermic technique may prove as difficult as the attainment of absolute zero, a feat of such difficulty that the last fraction of a degree to the absolute cessation of motion has not been negotiated. Immortality via the freezer may prove a cold trail. But even a portion of it may be worth the battle.

11 The Military Cyborgs

They were wearing shorts and T-shirts with large blue M's on their fronts, their limbs were exposed. Instead of arms and legs they had transparent extensions whose smooth surfaces shone in the sun. Each of these limbs was a tangle of metallic rods and coils, scattered all through each one were tiny bulbs which lit up and faded as the limb moved, sending off spatters of icy blue light. The strangers advanced a short distance into the open, arms and legs flashing as though, yes, as though they contained swarms of fireflies. And now something else: with each movement a very faint staccato sequence of clicks and clacks, an almost inaudible susurring, as of twigs snapping.

All of these men had four artificial limbs, always four, but the ones in front, the ones who had cleared the path through the jungle were wearing specialized instruments in place of their right arms. Some had what looked like flame-throwers, long tubes terminating in funnel-shaped nozzles which were still smoking, a moment ago they had been spitting out fifty-foot tongues of fire (the bassoons); others had long many-jointed claws on the ends of which were mounted high-speed rotary saws (the sopranos). Some twenty of these men emerged from the thicket. When they stopped, those in the lead pulled the tools from their arm stumps, picked up regular plastic arms which were hanging from their belts and snapped them into place in the empty sockets.

They stood in a group, surveying the village and the natives assembled in dead silence behind Ubu. They made no further move. Except for the blasting and cutting tools now dangling from their waists they seemed to have nothing even remotely resembling a weapon with them. They talked quietly among themselves, looking up to the sky from time to time as though expecting something there.

In a few seconds another group, aerialists, came into sight some forty or fifty feet over the tops of the raffia trees. Each was self-propelled; two counter-rotating rotors attached to an elongated right arm made each man a human helicopter.

Bernard Wolfe
Limbo
Ace Books, 1952.

137

It is obvious that the military produced some of the first human-artificial combinations that may be considered as crude cyborgs. The caveman with a club was not particularly sophisticated unless we compare him with the unarmed caveman he attacked. The first swords or lances were still relatively primitive extensions of human capability, although with the spear and other missiles man was learning how to make himself felt even at a distance.

The knight in armor of King Arthur's day, lance at the ready as he sat astride a charger likewise protected by a skirt of chain mail; represented a far more complex development of the military cyborg. Here man had added a protective coating to his body, converted his arm into a deadly weapon, and supplanted his own legs with four far sturdier ones. Galahad, whose pure heart endowed him with the strength of ten, without armor, lance and steed would have been about as puny as ordinary man in the physical strength department.

Later, the fighting man would be coupled with such contrivances as the tank to create a knight whose strength was as the strength of ten thousand or more of Arthur's finest and the airplane, which was a coupling yielding a still greater increase in destructive power. Good pilots "flew by the seat of their pants"; they literally became part of their machine. Some of the troubles of our giant and complicated aircraft today may be a lack of this intimacy between pilot and plane.

In World War II Japan introduced a new deadly weapon in the kamikaze pilot, joined to his craft for eternity in one last suicidal flight. Even more extreme was the "Baka" bomb, a bomb guided to its target not by a bombardier or external controls, but by a human steering device crammed into a cubbyhole and giving his life to deliver the bomb on target. These two developments must be classed as recessive cyborg types, freaks that do not reproduce their kind.

The military is concerned with another kind of cyborg as well: a man-machine it created in battle—the casualty. The same EMG principle that the Navy is investigating for remote control of weaponry—thus safeguarding human life and limb, of course—offers an ideal solution to the improvement of artificial limbs to patch up the casualties of past wars.

Far more money has been paid to veterans in bonuses, even to those who never saw fighting, than has been spent in rehabilitating those who lost limbs in the fighting. Representative Edith Nourse Rogers incurred the disfavor of many of her colleagues by bringing World War II amputees to sit in the galleries at Congress to call attention forcefully to their plight. Veterans themselves, including well-known columnist Robert S. Allen, himself a veteran and amputee, protested the ill-fitting and often completely useless artificial limbs tossed them after their loss. Partly because of such pressure, the Army, and the Navy too, has been able to advance the design of artificial limbs and see to it that veterans are fitted with replacements that make it possible for them to live lives somewhere near normal.

It is a fact of modern life that most scientific research is government supported, and a large part of the government's expenditures are for the military. It follows then that the military is keenly interested in fields like cybernetics, bionics, electromyography, and others allied with the cyborg idea. The services have active programs in biochemistry, cryobiology, physiological stress, electronics, and computer technology.

Beyond the humanitarian considerations that prompt its work in the field of patchwork prosthetics, the military is working toward exploiting the cyborg idea as a means of producing supersoldiers, and more sophisticated weapons and other systems. All branches, as we shall see, are active.

Weapons could be controlled remotely, aimed by simple movements of the operator's head or even his eyes, and triggered by a flick of the eyes or the thought, "Fire!" A forerunner to this remote control of weapons has already been tested. Control of "drone" helicopters from a distance is effected by head movements rather than operation of manual control devices. And a system to permit firing a weapon by a pilot simply by flicking his eyes is under study and seems to have possibilities. Man has only two hands, and often this is a serious complaint. EMG control, the operation of devices by simply thinking about them, frees the soldier from such shorthandedness and permits him a multitude of simultaneous operations instead of only one thing at a time.

We have mentioned the flier who flew by the seat of his pants and was part of his craft, or rather with it made up a cyborg device. It was an Air Force officer who coined the name "bionics," and one result of this wedding of living systems with artificial is the EMG muscle-boosting devices described in an earlier chapter. Here are other typical contracted projects the Air Force is sponsoring:

BIOLOGICAL LAWS AND EFFECTS. *Contractor: Adaptronics, Inc., Alexandria, Va.*

A compilation of biological laws, effects, and phenomena with associated physical analogs is being made on a continuing basis. The purpose is to help engineers to obtain information about biological systems for use in building more efficient machines.

VISILOG. *Contractor: General Electric, Ithaca, N.Y.*

The purpose is to use information obtained from studies of human perception to build a machine which can perform some of the functions of the human eye. These include avoiding collisions in unfamiliar territory by judging distances and time to contact.

ANALOG OF THE EAR. *Contractor: ITT Federal Laboratories, Nutley, N.J.*

A device is being constructed, using transmission line principles, which duplicated the important auditory functions of (1) conversion of signals from time domain to space domain; (2) frequency sensitivity; (3) signal-to-noise ratio enhancement. Further work will be directed toward utilization of the device as an input sensor to an adaptive network.

LIVING CELLULAR ANALOGS. *Contractor: Planned.*

Biological systems are composed of many different types of cellular elements (such as the neuron) that are required to perform vital functions. It is the purpose of this effort to understand the functions such cells play in biological systems and derive adequate physical analogs of such elements.

BIOLOGICAL MATERIALS AND PHYSICAL ANALOGS. *Contractor: Planned.*

In living systems, function or performance is often attributable to the material involved. A study of the similarities and dissimilarities of biological and physical materials is intended to reveal the most applicable physical analogs for the exploitation of the engineer.

MUSCLE SUBSTITUTE. *Contractor: Laboratory for Study of Sensory Systems, Tucson, Ariz.*

An artificial muscle is being developed to lift heavy loads short distances with very high (90% or better) efficiency. They may be useful especially under high-g conditions or under other conditions where muscles are absent or functioning poorly.

INTERCOMMUNICATION CONCEPTS AND COMPATIBILITY. *Contractor: Planned.*

Detailed knowledge of the compatibility of man and machines, in which men are an integral part of the system, is required. Methods must be found to increase the transfer rate of intelligence between man and machine in such systems.

The Air Force also has some man-machines that form a second-generation follow-on of the "mobot" or man-controlled mobile robot idea. Called Handyman and Beetle, these robots with men inside are designed to work on nuclear aircraft, to effect rescues of personnel from crashed planes, and to handle other similarly hazardous tasks. Inside the giant Beetle, which walks on ponderous caterpillar tracks, sits a human operator who is shielded by a thick skull of lead and special glass and is the brain of the machine.

The Navy's Cyborgs

The Air Force has no corner on the cyborg idea. In fact the Navy produced one of the most dramatic man-machine couplings yet known in its "frogmen." Far back in our history a pioneer submariner named David Bushnell converted himself into an undersea creature by climbing into a barrel-like craft he submerged and pedaled beneath the sea. With it he attempted to torpedo enemy ships, but was not too successful. But the frogman of the

1940's was a scourge beneath the waves and did succeed in delivering high explosives where they would do the most harm. In effect, man provided himself with webbed feet, eye protection, an artificial lung, and a new method of breathing so that he could survive in an otherwise fatal environment.

The deep-sea diver had pioneered in earlier years, a creature artificially able to withstand terrible pressures far beneath the surface—pressures in ghastly evidence when something went wrong with the pressure system of a diver's suit and the sea squeezed him jellylike into the steel helmet designed only for his head.

Evolutionists believe that man stems from life that emerged from the sea. The Book of Genesis in its first chapter promises man dominion over that sea. Interestingly, the U.S. Navy is currently conducting an undersea experiment called GENESIS I, hopefully a step toward realization of this promised mastery of the watery three-fourths of our world. The phase of this project in which human volunteers have been trained to breathe an atmosphere of helium and oxygen—rather than the nitrogen and oxygen we are accustomed to, and at seven times the pressure—has been completed. The subjects successfully spent six days at a simulated depth of 200 feet.

It required four days for the men breathing a helium mixture to learn to talk intelligibly with the new medium. Its effect on the voice produces a "Donald Duck" timbre and requires retraining to permit understanding. But this hurdle and the more important ones of adjusting to pressure were accomplished. The final phase of the GENESIS project will be living 180 feet underwater in a special "sea-lab" beneath the Navy's *Argus Island* research tower.

French underwater pioneer Jacques-Yves Cousteau has also conducted underwater living experiments, and these, along with even weirder experiments conducted by Russian and American scientists in training animals to *breathe* water, will be discussed in a later chapter.

Cyborg development underwater is proceeding in a roundabout

way. One result of atomic energy research was the mobile robot or manipulator with arms and hands controlled by a human operator from a safe distance. Here is the old "action at a distance," pioneered by the first man who ever tossed a rock, and improved upon by wire and other forms of communication. Hughes Aircraft Company built some of the early atomic energy manipulators that allowed men to handle dangerously radioactive materials safely from behind a thick glass shield. Hughes later developed underwater mobots for the Navy and for oil-drilling firms operating offshore wells. Fitted with television eyes and sonar ears, and coupled to a human operator by electric signals, such undersea extensions permit man to explore and work without subjecting his body to the dangers encountered beneath the sea.

We seem to be moving away from the intimate man-machine coupling that forms the most impressive sort of cyborg, but this great physical separation is very important to the cyborg concept. Effective though the man-controlled robot was, there was a lag at the "interface" between man and a machine. A human operator coupled with a mobot swimming through the sea five hundred feet below him watches a television screen and pushes buttons and turns knobs to control his extended arms and other physical appurtenances. But there is an inescapable loss of time between his seeing that an action is needed, telling his hand what to do, and the hand flicking the proper switch. The answer to that seems to be the elimination of the interface, and the Navy is very interested in the idea of using not the physical movements of a man's hands but the myoelectric signals present in his body.

In an earlier chapter we discussed the application of such signals to the Russian electronic hand. At first glance such a system seems only an electronic refinement of the older method of cineplasty, in which muscle itself operates a cable that moves a limb. But the miracle of electronics makes the distance between signal and thing to be moved of little importance. This important fact was dramatically suggested in an article in a technical journal published late in 1963. The title of the piece was "Navy Studying Control

of Weapons Through 'Thinking' of Them." The inevitable sub-
title was a coy "If looks could kill. . . ."

The Office of Naval Research contracted with the Philco Corporation for research into this possibility. Project officer was Dr.
James W. Miller. Philco experts at the firm's Bio Technology
Laboratory studied the problem and farmed out a phase of the
research to New York University. Dr. Renato Contini of the Research Division of the School of Engineering and Science was in
charge of this work involving monitoring of a subject by means of
electrodes attached to the skin over the muscles under study.
Such studies are similar to those of Lyman and others at UCLA.

Amplified EMG signals are routed to a computer, in this case
a Philco–2000, which displays them as a pattern that can be understood by the subject and help him to elicit the responses needed
for generating effective control signals. The project is officially
titled "Study to Investigate the Feasibility of Utilizing Electrical
Potentials on the Surface of the Skin for Control of Functions."

Walter L. Wasserman, manager of Philco's Bio Technology
Laboratory, describes the potential of the project:

> *Once we can establish the feasibility of control functions by sur-
> face bio-potentials, the results will open the door to many bio-control
> applications such as experimentation in electroneurographic signal
> identification, improvement of prosthetic devices (artificial limbs
> with far greater precise control than existing devices), remote control,
> control of field of vision, bio-controlled "man amplifier," walking
> vehicle control and control of motor functions under extreme G-loads.*

The idea of a bio-controlled "man amplifier" is being investigated for the Navy by Cornell Aeronautical Laboratories, which
has done earlier work for the Navy developing "perceptron"
machines, computer-like devices which perceive and learn.

Army Research

The Army too is interested in the idea of amplifying, or augmenting man's capabilities. The Army's Boston Ordnance Dis-

trict has contracted with General Electric for the development of giant walking machines to automate traditional footslogging dog-faces. While planes, helicopters, jeeps and amphibious craft have done much to get the infantryman off his aching feet, there remain times and terrains where only the act of walking will get the job done.

With giant twelve-foot legs, and perhaps six of these, the "pedipulators" as they are called will be controlled by the infantryman. The Army foresees such tasks as carrying supplies, fighting fires, effecting rescues and carrying litters of injured with artificial arms, again controlled by the man inside. General Electric engineers have applied the name "cybernetic anthropomorphic machines" to the walkers; man-shaped walking machines, that is. Mercifully this tongue-twisting technological name is generally shortened to an easy-to-say CAM. It will move across rough terrain not at the human pace of perhaps four miles an hour, but a blistering thirty-five. While the original concept was for the human operator to control his machine by walking himself, in a sort of cradle with pedals, it may be that the EMG idea will work well here too.

Traditionally, then, the military has fostered the idea of a cyborg joining of man and artificial extensions to his limbs and capabilities. There seems to be no change in that association in the future; if anything it will accelerate. The military services generally have fostered the man-machine idea with money and moral support more than have private ventures. Hopefully, the machine part of the cyborg fighting man of the future will be more and more in evidence until one day secondary evolution has progressed to the point where the machine does all the dangerous and dirty work. On the road to that goal however, the military quite likely will produce more and more sophisticated cyborgs—whose very thoughts can kill.

12 *Cyborgs in Space*

Those pessimists who make the mistake of comparing physical conditions of other planets with those of earth, considering as utterly uninhabitable worlds where beings of our species could not survive, do not use the reasoning of a philosopher—but that of a Fish. Fish reasoners, of course, are convinced that water is the sole element for life, that nothing can exist out of water.

> Kenneth Heuer
> *Men of Other Planets*
> Collier, 1951.

We have discussed cyborgs of different kinds: "medical" cyborgs and military cyborgs for example. However, perhaps the most intriguing man-machines will be those tailored for the newest of our frontiers, that of outer space. Man is creating a different environment here on earth but little that he does can match conditions beyond the planet. The extremes of temperature encountered by terrestrial man are as nothing to the absolute cold and searing heat in space. There is no atmosphere to provide air for breathing and protection from harmful radiation; instead space offers a "hard" vacuum. There is no weight in space for the free-falling astronaut, but before and after that part of his flight he is subject to violent accelerative forces. Added to these dangers are those of electromagnetic radiation, and of particles of matter in various sizes whizzing about.

Space obviously offers man a very hostile environment. Bernal, writing in 1929, was well aware of this. Pointing out that spatial conditions would be more favorable to mechanized man than organic man, he prophesied, "The colonization of space and the mechanization of the body are obviously complementary." Thirty years later, Manfred Clynes and Nathan S. Kline were thinking principally of space when they used the name cyborg. Kline is noted for his work with psychic energizers and other drugs, and received the Albert Lasker Award for medical research in 1964. Manfred Clynes is director of the Biocybernetics Laboratories at Rockland State Hospital in Orangeburg, New York. In May of 1960 the two scientists presented a paper at the Psychophysiological Aspects of Space Flight Symposium sponsored by the Air Force School of Medicine in San Antonio, Texas. The paper was subsequently published in the *Proceedings* of the symposium (Columbia University Press, 1961) under the title "Drugs, Space, and Cybernetics: Evolution to Cyborgs." A portion of the paper's introduction is given here:

> Participant Evolution. *The challenge of space travel to mankind is not only to his technological prowess, it is also a spiritual challenge to take part in his own biological evolution. The great scientific advances in the years to come may be utilized to permit existence under environments radically different from those provided by natural circumstances today. This task of adapting his body to whatever milieu he chooses will be made easier by increased knowledge of homeostatic functioning, the cybernetic aspects of which are just beginning to be investigated and understood. It is also likely that through a study of his psychological and physical needs in unusual environments a clearer understanding of man's needs in his home environment will be found.*
>
> *In the past, the altering of bodily functions to suit different environments was accomplished through evolution. From now on, at least in some degree, this can be achieved without alteration of heredity by suitable biochemical, physiological, and electronic modification of man's existing modus vivendi.*

Nature, the authors point out, finds various biological solutions in coping with the environmental problems of different living creatures. Man, hibernating animals, and a certain kind of fish whose blood takes on the temperature of its environment are examples of different degrees of accommodation. Mammals, fish, insects, and plants each have different solutions—solutions that have inherent limitations outside their specified field of operation. However, this is not an insurmountable problem. Suppose, say Kline and Clynes, that a fish wanted to live on the land. This desire and its fulfillment have occurred in nature over ages of time. But a particularly intelligent, dissatisfied fish who knew a lot about biochemistry and physiology and was a master engineer and cybernetician with necessary equipment would be able to fashion himself an instrument for breathing air.

For the fish simply to carry along a bubble of water to permit his normal breathing for a limited time would be shortsighted. Likewise, for man to carry along a bubble of air when he invades space is dangerous temporizing. The bubble, say the authors, all too easily bursts. A better approach is to adapt man to the environment of space.

Tackling the many specific problems facing man in space, the authors provide solutions that could be devised with existing knowledge, and also predict those which may be made in the future. Typical of these latter solutions is that for the problem of breathing in space: Don't breathe!

Describing space as "The New Frontier," Clynes and Kline say:

> If man attempts a partial adaptation to the conditions of space instead of being insistent that he carry his entire environment with him, a number of new possibilities appear. One is led to ask what are then the biologic changes that would have to be made in his homeostatic mechanism for man to be able to live in space qua natura?

A key to success is self-regulation of the new cyborg systems space travelers are provided with. If normal man had to consciously maintain the proper heart beat and blood pressure, breathing rate, digestive functions, and other self-regulating functions, he would have no time left for anything else. Similarly, if a cyborg spaceman has to make continual checks of the equipment that keeps him alive and effective in space, he is merely a slave to the machine attached to him. "The purpose of the Cyborg is to provide an organizational system in which these robot-like problems are taken care of automatically and unconsciously, thus freeing man to explore, to create, to think, and to feel. . . ."

As a starting point, the authors explore the "natural" human physiological and psychological performance of the raw material available. Yoga is mentioned, as well as hypnosis and the use of drugs to extend muscular control and other phenomena. Everything that man can do with the living equipment at hand should be exploited before physiological, mechanical, and electronic changes are begun.

Radiation damage seems an inevitable space hazard, and the authors feel that improved drugs should be developed to protect against its effects. Such drugs should be administered only when needed, and automatically by a servomechanism responsive to the radiation count.

Time is a problem in space flight. On short trips it might be advantageous or even required that the astronaut remain awake for long periods of time. Such wakefulness can be effected by psychic energizers. This medication also might have the advantage of reducing physiological and psychological stress. Clynes and Kline also point out that despite the science-fiction sound of it, trips of many years must be planned for. This poses a reverse problem from that of one demanding constant wakefulness.

On a flight of many years there would be little reason for the traveler to remain awake the entire trip. On the contrary, there are many reasons why he should do otherwise. Boredom is an obvious one. Another reason is the consumption of human fuel at an estimated rate of ten pounds a day per astronaut in the wakeful condition.

Fictional spacemen have long resorted to "suspended animation" to solve these problems of galactic flight. The time is at hand for real solutions. Lowered metabolism is the answer. The thyroid gland controls the body's living rate, and thus is a logical candidate for tampering. But the authors point out that antithyroid preparations tend to upset the operation of other endocrine organs, and some are possibly carcinogenic. Ablation of the thyroid also produces unwanted effects.

Hypothermia by physically cooling the body seems the most practical solution at present, with the later possibility of drugs to accomplish the same purpose. Clynes and Kline suggest an interesting possible hypothermia technique stemming from research by C. H. Li with the pituitary growth-hormone in rats. This substance acts differently on the brain than on other parts of the body, and in one experiment the rest of the body stopped growing while the brain did not. "Acromegaly," a chronic disease characterized by enlargement of hands, feet, or other parts of the body, is natural evidence of different body activity possible because of hormone stimulation. Perhaps an astronaut might be selectively treated so that while his body slept to conserve food, water, and air, his brain might remain active. As an alternative, the authors suggest that the entire spaceman be cooled "homeostatically," that is, via hypothermia or drugs. His brain only would be electronically heated to maintain its activity!

The possibility that hypothermia might also afford protection against radioactivity has been suggested. With long periods of hibernation, there is the question of what happens to the muscle tone of the hypothermic spaceman. Bears and other natural hibernators rouse from sleep with their strength capable of being restored by a few good meals. Perhaps this will prove the case with humans, although drugs may be required to artificially provide tonus for the quiescent muscles.

Breathing is a metabolic system suited to our atmosphere, but all wrong for space flight. The astronaut needs about two pounds of oxygen a day for normal breathing, and a one-year trip for three men would thus require carrying along a ton of oxygen. Ideally, an artificial organ should replace the lung, the authors suggest. This might consist of an "inverse fuel cell" that would convert CO_2 to C and O_2. Such a fuel cell could be powered by solar or atomic energy. One result of this change in man's plumbing would be that he not only wouldn't have to breathe, he *couldn't*. Operating as a closed system with the artificial lung, the spaceman would have no air with which to articulate speech sounds, and he would most likely be fed intravenously. He could just keep his mouth shut.

Cyborg technicians have only begun by adding an artificial lung. Body wastes are a problem in space and thus some drastic changes in plumbing are also in store. To obviate the need for drinking water, processed urine would be reshunted directly into the bloodstream, urea having been removed by a filter. Intravenous feeding and lowered metabolism would result in a much lower output of solid waste; sterilization of the gastrointestinal tract might largely eliminate it.

The cardiovascular system too must be modified in the cyborg. "By reason of different metabolic needs, as well as haemodynamic considerations, the biologically optimum heart rate and blood pressure under extraterrestrial conditions may be considerably different from that on earth," the authors wrote prophetically. This phenomenon is already of concern to Russian and American scientists with flights of only a few days having been made.

Hypothermia to produce lowered metabolism also drastically affects the operation of the heart and the circulation of the blood. The use of drugs and of electric stimulation may be necessary on the heart and also the brain to produce the desired cardiovascular functioning for survival in space.

One reason for the difference in heartbeat and blood pressure on earth and in space is the condition of weightlessness existing in orbital or "free-fall" flight. This phenomenon upsets more than the functioning of the heart. Even with the space ship rotated to produce artificial gravity, the situation is far different from that encountered on earth. As a result the balance or orientation mechanism of the ear's semicircular canals is thrown out of kilter, producing disorientation, nausea, and possibly vomiting.

Drugs might be used to reduce the sensitivity of the vomiting center, as is done terrestrially for seasick and airsick travelers. The vestibular organs might also be put out of commission intentionally by either draining off the endolymphatic fluid, or completely filling the cavities. Hypnosis is another possibility mentioned by the authors.

Allied with the vestibular function problem is that of visual perception. Weightlessness and the lack of any cues such as horizon or horizontal and vertical references destroys the frame of reference we are accustomed to. Therefore it is suggested that perhaps drugs that influence autokinesis may have an influence on the problem of perception in space.

Man in space is subjected to great temperature extremes. The lowering of body temperature for metabolism changes would have the beneficial effect of also suiting man better to the frigid cold of space darkness. However, some additional protection would be required from cold and also from heat and sunlight. The authors mention existing pharmaceuticals that produce changes in pigmentation and protect against actinic rays. Such a technique, automatically regulated in response to light striking the cyborg, might help maintain desired body temperature.

The absence of gravity poses great problems for the space man, as does even the lessening of this force. There is another problem in increased gravity such as will be found on some of the planets. This hints at the possible necessity of drastically altering man physiologically for survival on a planet like Jupiter.

There are many other problems that must be considered in space, including the possible effects of magnetic fields and the harmful results of sensory invariance and action deprivation that inevitably lead to boredom and even psychosis. Another problem is that of erotic and emotional satisfaction to which natural man is accustomed. Not just the physical body, but the mental attitude must be conditioned for survival in space. Perhaps "pleasure centers" in the brain may have to be stimulated electronically using the ESB technique (Electronic Stimulation of the Brain) reported experimentally by Dr. James Olds at UCLA.

Clynes and Kline conclude their paper with the following summary:

> It is proposed than man should use his creative intelligence to adapt himself to the space condition he seeks rather than take as much of earth environment with him as possible. This is to be achieved

through the Cyborg, an extension of organic homeostatic controls by means of cybernetic techniques. Both chemical and electronic means are to be used in the control systems to be built, which will cooperate with the body's own autonomic controls. The necessary change of these controls for space survival cannot be conveniently supplied for us by evolution; they have to be created by man himself, using his acquired knowledge of cybernetics and physiology. Thus, man's activity in this regard complements evolution, freeing him from the need of conscious attention to the regulation of his own internal environment.

NASA and the Cyborg

The two authors presented this paper in May, 1960. How prophetic it was is indicated in present work being done in the field of the cyborg by NASA. In August, 1962, that organization signed a contract with United Aircraft Corporation for a "Cyborg Study," a research project understandably termed the "most exotic of bioastronautic subjects."

After an initial eight-month phase, the Cyborg Study moved into a second stage in 1963. Included in investigations were biocybernetics, artificial organs, mineral dynamics, hypothermia, the use of drugs to affect the endocrine system, sensory deprivation and so on. Scientists point out that one drawback of deep hypothermia is that the subject might then need artificial cardiovascular and kidney systems to stay alive, much as Kline and Clynes had suggested. United Aircraft also feels that hypothermia studies for spacemen may result in "vast terrestrial fallout" of a beneficial nature.

A natural outcome of the Cyborg Study was the building by engineers of an experimental artificial heart, and construction of a cardiovascular system simulating that of an astronaut for study of blood flow, turbulence, pressure characteristics, as well as the mechanical details of pumps and valves in the artificial heart itself.

Another facet of varying environmental conditions is "hyperbaria," or subjection to an atmosphere of high pressure. One example is the treatment of a patient suffering from "bends," like a diver who is brought up too quickly from the depths of the sea. This subjection to extreme pressure can be used to cure gas gangrene, which is usually fatal when not so treated, to hasten the healing of burns, to eliminate infection, and to control bleeding. Hyperbaria forces extra quantities of oxygen into the tissues, and it is interesting to speculate on a hypothermic subject subjected to hyperbaria, thus supercharging him with oxygen and far increasing his capabilities.

The fantastic "human engineering" in prospect in preparing man for his assault on space seems tame compared with some of the predictions made by others in the field. For example, astronomer Kenneth Heuer in his book *Men of Other Planets* suggests that space travelers will have to be specially bred for the individual planet they are destined to fly to. And Dr. Eugene B. Konecci, director of NASA's Biotechnology and Human Research group, says, "Our understanding of the chemistry of genes may soon enable us to modify or enlarge organs, thus accelerating evolution to a state where man could successfully survive in strange environments."

These recent utterances are familiar echoes of the late Dr. William Olaf Stapledon, British scientist and writer on the idea of engineering men for planetary travel. For Jupiter, for example, Stapledon said:

> *By very drastic eugenical operation it might be possible to allow the human brain to be supported in spite of excessive gravitation, by throwing man into the quadruped position, pushing the head far backwards so as to distribute its weight evenly between the fore and hind legs. What about hands? The nose might be elongated into a trunk grasping instruments like fingers. The eyes would have to be projected well forward.*

All of which hardly sounds like progress, since man has only recently gotten himself up from all fours to walk erect!

Inner Space

Let us not forget inner space with all this attention to outer space. For hostile environment it is hard to beat what we have right here on earth beneath the surface of our seas. Pressure? Many tons of it per square inch. Air to breathe? Plenty of it, but it is locked in water and man must learn how to extract it. By now, he may have already done so. In 1961 Dr. John W. Severinghaus of the University of California Medical Center, San Francisco, and two medical student assistants taught rats to breathe water rather than air. And in the Russian publication *Komsomolskaya Pravda*, July 6, 1963, it was claimed that Soviet scientists had kept mice alive for twenty-four hours at the bottom of a tank of water. While neither Russian nor American scientists had solved the problem of making the physiological change reversible, reports from the University of Leyden in Holland claim just that. There, according to reports, a dog survived the return to a normal atmosphere after having learned to breathe water.

Jacques-Yves Cousteau is pioneering man's adaptation to undersea living in his "village" far beneath the surface in the Mediterranean. Perhaps one day we may have frogmen in the true sense of being amphibious beings.

There are those, of course, for whom the idea of the cyborg remains pure science fiction. Typical of scientists who hold the view that no such alterations of natural man will be necessary is Dr. Toby Freedman, Director of the Life Sciences Department at North American Aviation's Space and Information Systems Division. North American is building the Apollo spacecraft, which will carry three astronauts to the moon.

The redesign of human beings is an age-old fantasy, Freedman says. Humorously he describes "an indestructible polyethylene heart, kidneys exchangeable every 50,000 miles, cavity-proof ceramic teeth, and nylon hair you comb only once in a lifetime." A physician, he is not optimistic over hopes for late-model, improved versions of man, pointing out that he has yet to see a machine with the durability of the human heart. Rather than adopt cyborg techniques, Freedman believes that man can be made to perform much better than he does without fitting him with a lot of internal gadgets. He cites the Eskimo and Bedouin as examples of temperature tolerance in natural man.

The scientific consensus, however, seems to be on the other side of the argument. Even before man-made orbital flights, experts were predicting nausea, balance upsets, ill effects from sensory deprivation, changes in sleep and other patterns, impairment of the circulatory system, and muscle and bone atrophy. Experience of astronauts has borne out this concern. Major Gordon Cooper reportedly was near fainting when he got out of the capsule after less than a day and a half of flight. Even nine hours had affected the blood pressure of Walter Schirra. Titov of Russia suffered from dizziness, loss of appetite, and nausea on his twenty-five hour flight, and the astronauts who made longer flights of up to five days reportedly showed adverse effects so serious that Russian doctors fear that long space flights may actually render the astronaut unable to resume life under natural gravity conditions.

The final answer to the debate on how much tinkering will be needed to safeguard man for space flight will be known only on successful accomplishment of such missions. But the case for the cyborg seems strong, and growing with new data.

13 *Tissue Culture*

DOMIN: *Now, the thing was how to get the life out of the test tubes, and hasten development and form organs, bones and nerves, and so on, and find such substances as catalytics, enzymes, hormones, and so forth, in short—you understand?*

HELENA: *Not much, I'm afraid.*

DOMIN: *Never mind. You see, with the help of his tinctures he could make whatever he wanted. He could have produced a Medusa with the brain of a Socrates or a worm fifty yards long. But being without a grain of humor, he took it into his head to make a vertebrate or perhaps a man. This artificial living matter of his had a raging thirst for life. It didn't mind being sewn or mixed together. That couldn't be done with natural albumin. And that's how he set about it.*

HELENA: *About what?*

DOMIN: *About imitating nature. First of all he tried making an artificial dog. That took him several years and resulted in a sort of stunted calf which died in a few days. I'll show it to you in the museum. And then old Rossum started on the manufacture of a man.*

Karel Čapek
R.U.R.
Oxford, 1923.

Thus far we have been discussing in some detail the replacement of human parts by two methods. In one method man substitutes a mechanical part for the missing living part. In the other, he replaces a lacking part with a living transplant taken either from the body of the patient or from a living donor of the same species or even of a different species.

There is a third method, even more sophisticated than the others, that may be used to provide replacement parts, or even additional or "different" parts as man sees fit to use them. This is "tissue culture," the growing of living cells in the laboratory rather than the parent body.

The word "tissue" to most of us connotes a thin layer of material, usually the skin. However, the skin is only one of the four types of tissue. *Epithelium* comprises skin and lining material. *Connective* tissue is bone, cartilage and, perhaps surprisingly, our blood. *Muscle* is a distinctive type of tissue, and we remember that it makes up the bulk of our body weight. Finally, there is *nervous* tissue, comprising our nerves, which includes the brain. Our entire bodies then are composed of tissue.

Man can survive as an individual; a single cell cannot unless it is somehow provided with the nutrients needed. There are some 90 of these substances in our bodies. In the play, *R.U.R.*, robots resembling men are "grown" in vats in a factory. This fantastic science-fiction concept lagged far behind fact, however. Long before author Karel Čapek put pen to his diatribe against the machine, Dr. Alexis Carrel was growing bits of chicken heart in a laboratory "broth" of the proper chemicals.

Comparing man's engineering and production capabilities with those of nature, Carrel wrote admiringly of the latter:

An organ builds itself by techniques very foreign to the human mind. It is not made of extraneous material, like a house. Neither is it a cellular construction, a mere assemblage of cells. It is, of course, composed of cells as a house is of bricks. But it is born from a cell, as if the house originated from one brick, a magic brick that would set about manufacturing other bricks. Those bricks, without waiting for the architect's drawings or the coming of the bricklayers, would assemble themselves and form the walls. They would also metamorphose themselves into windowpanes, roofing-slates, coal for heating, and water for the kitchen and the bathroom. An organ develops by means such as those attributed to fairies in the tales told to children in bygone times. It is engendered by cells which, to all ap-

pearances, have a knowledge of the future edifice, and synthesize from substances contained in blood plasma the building material and even the workers.

Tissue Culture

This idea of bits and pieces of creatures "living" under completely artificial conditions was—and is—most distasteful to some people. The thought of a chicken's heart made immortal flies in the face of theology, morality, and common sense. But persevering researchers have grown cells of various types, learning much about biology in the process.

At first it was possible to cultivate cell tissue only on a "substrate" or solid base such as glass or cellophane, but in 1954 a new technique was developed in which cells were grown in liquid. By 1956, tissue culture studies had turned up the amazing fact that man's genetic inheritance stems from only forty-six chromosomes and not the forty-eight that textbooks had preached as nature's gospel.

Tissue culture advanced our knowledge of cancer and gave clues to fighting the disease. It told us much about heredity, aging, and other interesting phenomena. But it was used primarily as an experimental technique, as research into other things. Only fictionally did anyone pursue the idea of tissue growing to produce a product in quantity. Frederik Pohl and C. S. Kornbluth wrote a science-fiction novel called *The Space Merchants* in which food was produced by growing tissue in a food factory. Nicknamed "Chicken Little" because it was anything but that, a giant chunk of protein was continually butchered by workers wielding huge knives. Here was Carrel's chicken heart carried out to full promise.

In 1962 Melpar, Inc. of Fairfax, Virginia, began development of an automated tissue-culture plant. Where earlier efforts had been on a small scale, producing tissue for medical research, Melpar's tissue "factory" aimed at production quantities on an automatic and carefully controlled basis.

Automated tissue culture at Melpar is a five-step process:

1. A technician obtains a sample of the desired tissue, taking it from the plant or animal—or human.

2. Measured amounts of tissue, together with the proper nutrients, are placed in a sealed tube.

3. In the desired artificial environment, with pressure, temperature, humidity, and nutrients carefully controlled, the tissue grows. This growth may be accelerated or altered by the controls imposed upon it.

4. Growth is accurately monitored during the process. Feedback technique guarantees that the product is identical in structure with the original sample used as a standard.

5. Harvesting is carried out automatically, sometimes by vibration devices that sort particles of tissue by size. Refrigeration and sealed containers guarantee absolute purity of the mature tissue.

There are a number of possibilities for such a tissue factory. One application is the production of food for astronauts during a space voyage. Meat, vegetables, and fruit would be produced. After each harvest, a small amount of tissue "starter" would be left in the unit so that it could grow into another crop.

The tissue factory takes the place of the natural environment, and also of the natural whole plant or body that normally makes it possible for the cells to live. The implications here are very important, since it is possible to "grow" vegetables, say, without the stems, roots, leaves, and skin normally associated with them. Meat without bone, fat, or gristle could be produced, and in any desired shape as well to simplify packaging. Foreseeable is a food factory in which chemical nutrients and solar energy nurture the starter tissue to produce the entire growing, harvesting, processing, and packing—all under one roof with no waste or lost motion.

This application is off the main path we are pursuing, of course. Our main concern here is the use of tissue growth to supply material for patching up or augmenting the human body; tissue banks of the future may well be stocked not from cadavers but from material grown in plants like that being pioneered by Melpar.

Another use more relevant to the cyborg concept is the growing of vaccines, gamma globulin, plasma, and so on. Hormones could be produced artificially and at accelerated rates, and skin grown for transplants. A sample of the patient's own tissue might be used for the starter material, or it may be possible to grow tissue that does not trigger the immune reaction, so that one universal type of lab-grown tissue could be used on all patients.

As we have noted, surgeons have "grown" new ears for patients by placing a perforated mold filled with diced human cartilage tissue in the patient's abdominal cavity. This technique might be used in the tissue culture lab to turn out finished ears on a production basis. Or sheets, slabs, and blocks of tissue could be grown and used to carve, mold, or shape the desired replacement grafts.

Since all of the body is tissue of one type or another, it would seem that replacements for any part of the body can be grown in the lab. Bone, bone marrow, and even corneal tissue might be grown.

An interesting aspect of cell growth is "differentiation," the ability of a single cell to grow into a final result of complex and varied form and purpose. Lower life forms have the property of regrowing a lost tail, limb, or even a body, as in the case of worms. This is believed possible because the animal has not progressed as far along the evolutionary scale and thus has not become so specialized a creature as man, who does not retain the ability to regrow a lost part. Work with tissue culture aids in the investigation of this property, and there is wistful and wishful talk of artificially inducing it in humans.

If it is possible to grow undifferentiated tissue, is it possible to have differentiation take place? We have kept organs alive and growing in artificial environments and the question comes up as to whether or not we could start with just a few of the proper cells and grow a heart.

There are more amazing possibilities—artificial conception in the laboratory and even tinkering with the genes to produce the sort of humans we want. And finally the idea of creating life itself with nature's raw materials, a possibility some scientists believe is within man's grasp as he probes deeper into the DNA molecule that seems to hold the key he seeks.

Reproducing Life

For all of man's effectiveness in repairing and altering his mind and body, it must be admitted that these changes he has wrought are after the fact. Participant evolution to date has been a sterile thing, and successive generations have reverted to genetic type. A much more effective job could be done by getting at the root, or rather the basic cell of the product he is trying to improve.

Much of the work of creating a cyborg is simply to repair or alleviate an inherent shortcoming in man. False teeth, eyeglasses, hearing aids, cardiac pacemakers, artificial kidneys, electronic hands, hydraulic legs, elevator shoes—all these things are commendable but the cure is of a short-lived nature. Ailing hearts kill off more of us prematurely than any other cause. We might advance artificial organ technology and production to the point where all of us can be fitted with superior plastic and metal replacements that will guarantee long and active lives. But meantime life becomes more and more dependent on a complex and artificial system. A war or some other great catastrophe could wipe out a cyborg civilization completely and then it would be many generations before we again clambered up the technological steps to regain our position.

A more lasting solution would seem to be the artificial creation of a better *natural* man. Rather than patch him up after he is born, why not produce superior men to begin with? Men with sturdier hearts, stronger backbones, more reliable kidneys and so on. This was the original plan, of course, and this is why man is different today from the way he was half a million years ago. Given time, nature will make the needed changes as she has in the past. And until recently, there was plenty of time for nature, who is not often in a hurry. In fact the surest test of an improvement is time itself. Mutations appear that seem to be beneficial, but die out because they are not ready for the world, or the world for them. Nature's drive toward evolution is evident in its very fecundity. Why else would there be such teeming numbers of the species that abound on our planet? If nature were satisfied with her handiwork would she not be content with a respectable number of men, animals, and other living things? From a natural standpoint, pastoral North America prior to infiltration by Columbus would seem a far happier state of affairs than the present crowded, confused civilization that has resulted. But this confusion stems from the proliferation of man.

The more living things there are, the more changes in them can be effected and experimented with—to be retained if good and dropped if otherwise. Nature is prodigal with her seed. Some living things produce eggs by the millions because otherwise a hostile environment would not permit sufficient of them to survive. Man, by comparison, has been called a very inefficient breeder. First, it takes two humans to reproduce, unlike the single-sexed earthworms who impregnate each other in their mating and both produce offspring. And while man makes sperm by the millions or billions, and could sire an estimated three thousand youngsters, a woman can bear a maximum of only about thirty during her productive years, barring multiple births. Actually, as many as half a dozen children per family is unusual.

Had it not been for the fact that man learned how to think about his world and act on those thoughts, all his reproductive capacity would doubtless have been necessary barely to keep even and provide the needed raw material for evolution through the ages. But having started to meddle in his own affairs, man has produced a world far less inimical to his existence. One result is described as the population explosion.

Faced with overcrowding, food shortages, social considerations, and the like, man has applied himself with some effectiveness to the task of artificially rectifying the situation. Unlike the lesser animals, he learned the detachment necessary in the middle of the heat of generation to thwart nature. In some of these ways, like Onan's, there was no mechanical contraception, no interposition of an artificial device, but simply the application of knowledge as to what caused children. Later came methods involving a more artificial barrier. Substances ranging from camel saliva to salt were introduced to prevent the sperm from reaching the ovum, or to kill the sperm rather than let it do its job of fertilization.

The importance of contraception should not be underestimated for it immediately sets man apart from the other inhabitants of the world and gives him a forceful weapon in the "power of death." Not the power of life, surely, but at least the power to make life for those *not* snuffed out a better one than it would be otherwise.

Man created a new species, in both sexes, with his attempts at curbing the birth rate. The male or female using a contraceptive is only temporarily a variant, nonreproducing human, but we have permanently sterile beings too. In women this change is effected through surgery or the permanent insertion of an "intrauterine contraceptive device" or IUCD. Japanese women have tolerated these "prostheses" for periods of twenty years with no harmful effects, other than that they bore no children.

In the early days of artificial tampering with the sexual activities of humans, young males were sometimes rendered incapable of the sex act with a male version of the chastity belt. In this operation a wire was passed through the foreskin and locked with a seal. A bit inhumane, the operation never really caught on, and modern men who desire an end to child production often submit to the painless surgery of vasectomy, in which the vas deferens is severed so that the sperm is not ejaculated during intercourse.

While many practice birth control in a number of ways, and many others would if they could, there remain those humans who are denied the privilege of having children and do everything they can to change *this* state of affairs. Fortunately the medical profession, which knows how to prevent conception, can often materially aid the chances for that event.

At times it is necessary to resort to artificial insemination, the having of a "test-tube baby." Artificial insemination in cattle is a standard practice, used to make the process of breeding more convenient for cattle raisers, if not more pleasant for the animals involved, and to produce better strains through using selected bulls as sperm donors. A similar technique is used with humans wishing children, with a specimen taken artificially from husband or other male donor and artificially placed in proximity to the ovum in the mother-to-be.

Extensions of this idea lead to such things as the transplanting of a fertilized egg from the natural mother to the womb of a host mother in animals, setting up of sperm banks for cattle, and so on. Through selective animal breeding, man has produced animals it would have taken nature ages to yield, if they ever occurred at all.

The test-tube baby is perhaps as close as man has come to the great ideal of eugenics fathered by Darwin's cousin, Sir Francis Galton. An amazing man, Galton was an expert on heredity, invented the idea of using fingerprints for identification, produced the ultrasonic "dog whistle" humans can't hear, and did a lot of other things. His great idea, however, was that of eugenics, the improvement of man through selective breeding. Galton was aware that in general the most intelligent people had the least children. This he was sure, would lead to the ruin of man, or at least his reversion to the old, animal ways. The answer, obviously, was for society to prevent men and women unfit for having children from mating productively, and fostering childbearing in the physically and intellectually superior.

The grand idea of eugenics has not yet succeeded. Galton himself was a prime example of the reason why: one of the most intelligent men of his or any time, he left no children to carry on his genetic strain. It was the old story of being able to lead the camel to the water of truth, but not being able to make him drink from it.

Another reason lies in the incomplete reasoning by Galton on the subject of genetics. It sometimes happens that a genius is born of parents who hardly know enough to come in out of the rain, and fortunately did not know how to prevent his conception. For all man's seeming knowledge, nature now and then proves she knows far more.

So eugenics fails in practice, and probably in theory as well. In its place man has resorted to "euthenics," promoting good health and well-being a posteriori in whatever raw materials nature chooses to provide him with. This compromise solution works wonders, as evidenced in the increased height and weight of humans in a relatively short period of time with better diet and other environmental conditions. Even intelligence has flourished where men are free to think instead of fighting hunger and disease with all their strength.

All of which is not to say that everyone has given up on the eugenics notion. Dr. Herman J. Muller is among those who suggest such Huxleyan ideas as a sperm bank stocked with specimens from the geniuses of our times, frozen for use even twenty years in the future to produce a continuing and improving race of supermen.

Dr. Muller is entitled to speak, having won the Nobel Prize in Medicine in 1946 for his work in the field of heredity. Muller, in experiments with the banana fly, found that mutations could be caused by exposure to X-rays, resulting in sudden great changes in genetic structure.

The test-tube method makes its possible for a baby to be conceived in an unnatural fashion. There are apocryphal tales, such as that of Civil War days in which a Minié ball struck a young officer in his vitals, spattering parts of them on a young woman next in line of the projectile's trajectory and thus impregnating her so that she bore a child. Such stories are perhaps of the whole cloth, or cover-ups for more natural conceptions enjoyed by participants who later rued what they had done and sought an out. At any rate, we *are* moving from the necessity of lovemaking in the production of children. There are even cases on record of parthenogenesis: the conception of a child by a female with no male help at all.

Parthenogenesis takes place in nature in other species. Bees, rotifers, plant lice, aphids, and brine shrimp are examples. Some writers have pointed to the possibility of a takeover by a race of superwomen with no need of mere man to propagate themselves. However, this fear is hardly grounded in fact. More probable is the production of real test-tube babies, in which conception and subsequent growth of the embryo takes place not *in utero* but in the laboratory.

The idea of removing a partially developed baby from the mother and growing it artificially arouses no great protest; it is done in the name of humanity every day in all our hospitals. Short-term infants are saved by incubators and skillful care even when taken from their mothers many months before normal birth.

Researchers with animals, particularly baby chicks, have also performed amazing surgery on embryos, substituting bits of brain tissue as though they were interchanging the pieces of a jigsaw puzzle. Admittedly at a crude stage of development, such surgery has resulted in living chicks of a vastly different type from those originally conceived in the egg. With such drastic embryonic manipulation possible, the idea of simply growing a fertilized egg in the laboratory occasions no great surprise. The actual fertilization does, however.

As long ago as 1944, Dr. John Rock at Harvard succeeded in artificially fertilizing an isolated human egg cell with donor sperm in the laboratory. Cell growth continued for as long as six days in these experiments, but maintenance of proper conditions to sustain life was not possible, or perhaps not even known. The growth of a living thing from its single cell is nature's most amazing miracle, and also her most guarded secret.

In 1958 a doctor in Italy took up the idea of the artificial womb. Dr. Danielle Petrucci at Bologna had for a number of years transplanted glands from animals into ailing human patients. Since 1952 he had replaced human pituitary glands with those taken from freshly killed calves. To insure speed in such operations he transported his patients right to the abbatoir. He claimed clinical success for his surgery in both men and women.

Delicate as the pituitary transplants were, they were simple operations compared with the process of achieving artificial contraception in a "ripe" ovum in the laboratory. Involved were three problems most workers held insurmountable: temperature, gas exchange phenomena and metabolism. Dr. Petrucci and his assistants, Dr. Laura de Pauli and Raffaele Bernaboo, tried again and again, slowly refining their techniques.

By 1961 they had succeeded to some extent no less than forty times. Obtaining ripe ova from women patients, Petrucci placed them in a depression in a glass slide, covered them with another glass slide and heated the assembly to precisely 97.7 F. Fluid containing sperm from a donor was then dripped onto the edge of the slides and drawn into the glass "womb" by capillary action. Conception took place when the sperm entered the waiting egg.

Carefully maintaining the proper temperature, Petrucci fed the developing embryo on oxygenated amniotic fluid taken from pregnant women. Finally one of the real test-tube embryos lived for twenty-nine days, growing from microscopic size to about that of a pea. At this stage of development it was noticed that growth was not proceeding according to nature's plan, but becoming "monstrous" and life was therefore terminated. Because Petrucci was a Catholic and knew—or thought he knew—what must be done, he gave the embryo conditional baptism and extreme unction.

A news announcement of the "success" of the experiment was made on January 13, 1961 and touched off a tempest in the church. *L'Osservatore Romano*, the Vatican's semiofficial newspaper, denounced the experiment as sacrilegious. A member of Catholic Action, himself a scientist, echoed this judgment, as did Radio

Vatican. In the U.S., the Catholic magazine *America* was even more explicit in its condemnation. "The spirit of Frankenstein did not die with the Third Reich," it said. "His blood brothers often wear the garb of Dr. Kildare and regard a human being as just another expendable microbe, provided it is legally defenseless, physically helpless, and tiny enough to ride on the stage of a microscope."

Professor Luigi Gedda, formerly head of Catholic Action and director of a genetics institute said, "Experiments of this kind do not take into due account the spiritual values of the human being."

In the magazine *America's* eyes, the fertilized ovum must be considered a human being, "endowed with all the panoply of natural and inalienable rights that are grounded in the simple fact of existence. The human person is a sacredness hedged round by a mantle of dignity and inviolability no matter whether it is cradled in a father's arms, nestled in a mother's womb, or floats in a test tube at the threshold of visibility."

Finally, the *America* article noted three strong points of protest:

1. *The experimenter who creates human life in a test tube deliberately places a person in an environment where the most basic and vital requirements of human nature cannot conceivably be met in the current state of medical science. To produce a human being, holding it captive like a genie in a bottle, and doom it to inevitable death is to exercise an irresponsible dominion that cannot be justified by any appeal to the common welfare of mankind or to the advancement of scientific goals.*

2. *If the experimenter knowingly terminates his experiment, he compounds his original irresponsibility with the malice of abortion—the calculated destruction of an inviable fetus.*

3. *Most abhorrent of all, to induce life in a test tube is to remove human generation from its essential biological purpose and effectively separate it from the mystery of loving unity with which God providentially surrounded it.*

L'Osservatore Romano noted on January 14 that "Scientific progress can't constitute an ultimate end . . . authorizing indiscriminately any kind of way and any kind of method!"

Trapped between opposing forces of science and theology, Dr. Petrucci attempted to defend the position of himself and his co-workers. He felt he had been grossly and unfairly misunderstood, and that he had done nothing immoral. The work he was doing with his test-tube conception was toward learning a way to combat the immune reaction in organ transplants, he stated.

"I have pursued scientific research for the bettering of the human race," he argued, notwithstanding *America's* comment to the contrary. "My goal was not the creation of life and I have not actually done that. I am a Catholic, and I know my duties, both as a religious man and as a scientist."

Dr. Petrucci's fate, however, was similar to that of the priest-scientist in Morris West's *Shoes of the Fisherman* whose scientific views ran counter to doctrine. Father Giuseppe Bosio, a Jesuit biologist to whom Petrucci turned, refused his support, pointing out in the Jesuit publication *Civiltà Cattolica*, that Pope Pius had spoken out explicitly against test-tube fecundation such as Petrucci was guilty of. Thus Petrucci had neither the right to start a life *in vitro* nor the right to put an end to it! In fact, once he *had* started it he was morally bound to do all he could to continue the life of the embryo.

Petrucci countered by quoting St. Thomas Aquinas to the effect that the soul did not enter the embryo for a matter of weeks; thus there was no guilt in his experiment. But in the end, faced with a solid wall of Roman Catholic opposition, Petrucci announced that he was suspending his experiments in test-tube embryo work.

America does not speak authoritatively for the church, but there is an interesting implication in its first point, which states that the "present state of science" cannot meet with the requirements of the test-tube embryo. If science *were* so able, would the experiment then be permissible? The paradox is that science cannot fit itself if it sticks to the dicta of the church.

Let us consider the future of the fetus *in vitro*, however, as if it will come to pass as an accepted technique. We have seen that genetic evolution has left its traumatic scars on us. These scars include a birth canal in women that is not quite large enough in most cases. Man—humane and perhaps guilt-ridden—does what he can with surgery, mechanical instruments, drugs and other artificial devices to make birth easier on the mother and safer for the child. Such considerations, as well as those which have substituted the bottle for the breast in most civilized society, suggest the inevitable adoption of the test-tube technique. If the father need feel no pain, why should the mother?

In the future we may have children the "sensible, modern way." After conception—in the old-fashioned way—the fertile egg will be removed surgically and placed in the laboratory "womb." Or perhaps both egg and sperm will be obtained artificially and joined together in the laboratory. Nine months—or whatever proves to be the optimum time—later, the happy parents will be presented with a bouncing baby, perhaps of whichever sex they choose.

With such techniques, the eugenics idea will be more possible of carrying out. Improving contraceptive methods may remove the last possibilities of accidental conception and all babies be produced on the assembly line, à la *Brave New World*. The population control will be a matter for the computer to work out and we will balance deaths with births, and also assure a mate for everyone while we are at it.

Perhaps even Dr. Muller's suggestion of frozen sperm in banks so that women decades hence can be fertilized by the great men will come to pass. The big question may be who are the greats? In the James Costigan play, *Baby Want A Kiss*, a male character visualizes frozen Celebrity Seed, packaged and made available to all women who want a child by their favorite star.

The test-tube baby, conceived and nurtured in the laboratory without benefit of sexual passion or a mother's womb might seem the ultimate in "artificial" man. It is not, however, as we shall see in the following chapter. Tiny as the egg and sperm are, they are composed of far tinier elements and man would like very much to tinker with these genes. The human body is built from nature's raw material, "programmed" by DNA molecules. Not content even with growing nature's seed in the laboratory, scientists are pondering the problem of poking at the seed itself, with an eye to engineering a crop of better men.

14 *The Gene Tinkerers*

Mr. Foster was only too happy to give them a few figures.

Two hundred and twenty metres long, two hundred wide, ten high. He pointed upwards. Like chickens drinking, the students lifted their eyes toward the distant ceiling.

Three tiers of racks: ground floor level, first gallery, second gallery. The spidery steel-work of gallery above gallery faded away in all directions into the dark. Near them three red ghosts were busily unloading demijohns from a moving staircase.

The escalator from the Social Predestination Room.

Each bottle could be placed on one of fifteen racks. Each rack though you couldn't see it, was a conveyor travelling at the rate of thirty-three and a third centimetres an hour. Two hundred and sixty-seven days at eight metres a day. Two thousand one hundred and thirty-six metres in all. One circuit of the cellar at ground level, one on the first gallery, half on the second, and on the two hundred and sixty-seventh morning, daylight in the Decanting Room. Independent existence—so called.

"But in the interval," Mr. Foster concluded, "we've managed to do a lot to them. Oh, a very great deal." His laugh was knowing and triumphant.

Aldous Huxley
Brave New World
Harper, 1932.

The construction of electronic hands and electromechanical hearts, remarkable as these feats surely are, is childishly simple compared with the idea of an entire artificial man created in the laboratory with synthetic chemicals of life juggled by "genetechnicians" to suit their purposes. Engineers have long looked hopefully at nature's method of building things and wished to duplicate it in the manufacture of electronic equipment and more mundane arti-facts. But the idea of preempting nature by building *men* boggles the minds of most of us. Not all, however.

Today not only science fiction, which has been plugging the idea for decades, but the popular press, which has gleefully mounted the genetic bandwagon, and the learned journals, whose pages are more fantastic than science fiction—all hail the possi-bility of artificially created life. Medical and science writers head-line their pieces, "Race of Super Men May Be Possible," "Secret of Life Unraveled!" with no apparent self-consciousness.

In bits and pieces scientists have indeed created life. The basic elements needed for life have been produced in the laboratory from lower forms by duplicating physical conditions thought to prevail in pre-amoebic days. Mutations have been created arti-ficially with radiation and with drugs, both intentionally and ac-cidentally. Man can effect fertilization of the human cell *in vitro* and grow tissue handily in the clinical sterility of a "white room." Even the very "secret of life," the gene, has been duplicated arti-ficially. Does it not then follow that he can create life?

The Gene

Philosophers have suggested that certain things are unknowable; that hard as man might study himself there are some secrets that will forever be withheld. Nevertheless scientists today are pur-suing the greatest mystery of all, the mystery of life itself. Sur-prisingly they are hot on the trail and even those not given to rash predictions feel that in a few years man will have the ability to alter life as we know it and even to create life in new forms. While many deplore even the thought of such power, claiming it to be sacrilegious in the extreme, after all the time, effort, and money man has spent finding ways to destroy life, attempts to *create* it seem commendable.

Feverish is not an extreme description for the activity proceed-ing in most laboratories equipped for genetic research, principally with the nucleic acids that are slowly proving themselves to be the blueprints, or coded instructions with which a single egg cell is able to grow into a plant, a bird, or a human. With our penchant for acronyms, we have called the two key acids DNA and RNA.

Years ago the Augustinian monk Gregor Mendel was among those who inquired into the why of nature and heredity. Because of limited knowledge and a nearly nonexistent technology for microscopic investigation, Mendel's work was mostly at the level of effect. He laid down the laws that tell us what offspring will result in following generations if we breed certain types of plants, or animals. Today man is more inquisitive, and he has the tools to follow up his nosiness. As a result he is digging eagerly at the *cause* of life, and even has the effrontery to try to copy it, to actually synthesize life. Fantastic as it seems today—it would have been labeled utterly impossible yesterday—he has already succeeded with crude forms. He has artificially duplicated a virus, he has created synthetic DNA and enzymes. Probing at molecules, he is impatiently perfecting equipment to let him see even the atoms of the genes. Finally, he plans to use this deciphered "blueprint" with the readily available building blocks of nature to produce artificial life.

As we have seen, laboratories are already growing tissue artificially, with a goal of tomatoes with no vine, steaks without bones and human corneal material and tissue for other grafts. Man will start with nature's blueprint, but then he may progress to juggling the specifications a bit to change the instruction code of the DNA to eliminate cancer and other defects in humans, and even to create completely new and different forms of life. This breakthrough may change our lives in the most literal meaning of that expression. The importance of DNA began to be realized only in the 1940's and man has not even been close to a rough idea about the growth of living things for much more than 100 years.

For most of our evolutionary history, we have been concerned primarily with staying alive and having children to keep the human race going. It was only as we progressed socially and scientifically that it became possible to investigate effectively just what man is and how he got that way. The nineteenth century marks the age when science finally got into gear in its probing into life itself.

In the 1830's German biologists advanced the cell theory of life. Much smaller building blocks were known or at least guessed at far earlier than this; *atom* is a Greek word dating back to Democritus. But cells are nevertheless so tiny that it takes a good microscope to see them. The largest human cell known, the egg cell that grows to be the mature adult, measures only about 1/200 of an inch in diameter.

In 1866 Mendel formalized the laws of inheritance that were a big step on the road to an understanding of life. Also in the nineteenth century came the theory of evolution propounded by Darwin, and the germ theory of disease advanced by Pasteur. Mendel was a botanist by avocation, and he carefully studied the results of crossing different strains of peas. He found that the varieties resulting in succeeding generations of plants were not random, but obeyed mathematical rules. Coloring, size, and other characteristics depended entirely on heritage of the plants, although the rules were complex enough to be evident only after long, careful study and bookkeeping.

Mendel's pioneering scientific work caused no great amount of interest, and gathered dust for many years. Its true meaning and worth were not discovered until much later when other scientists had learned enough pursuing their research to appreciate what Mendel was saying. By then they saw that the laws of inheritance applied not just to peas and beans, but to birds, horses, and even men.

As we have said, Mendel dealt with effects. Scientists could only infer the causes, working backward as it were. They found that there were chromosomes and genes—from whence comes the name genetics—involved in the growth of living things. But the key to it all, the Rosetta stone of life escaped them. Strangely, that key had been discovered just three years after Mendel formulated his laws, but it too went unused for decades until science learned how to investigate further.

In 1869 Friedrich Miescher, a German researcher, discovered an unknown substance in tissue he was studying in his laboratory. Unable to identify it, he gave it the name "nuclein" since he had found it in the nucleus of the cell. Unfortunately, it would be about sixty years before the tremendous importance of his discovery was learned.

In working with viruses in the 1930's, W. M. Stanley, an American biochemist, isolated the "tobacco-mosaic" strain. These tiny organisms were far too small to be seen even in a microscope and passed through the finest filters available. It was obviously quite a trick just to capture the wily disease-producing bug and Stanley later shared a Nobel Prize for his feat. Meantime, there were some remarkable things learned about the isolated virus. First, it was not made up of cells but more resembled a chromosome, the tiny characteristic determinant of the cell; second, it could "replicate," or reproduce itself inside a cell; and finally, it contained Miescher's discovery, nuclein, which had since come to be called nucleic acid.

Science is often like detective work. Given bits and pieces of information, researchers put them together to get the answers they seek or at least stronger clues toward those answers. This was the case with the tobacco mosaic virus that so strangely resembled a chromosome. The key to genetics, the blueprint of the growth of cells into a "finished product" not just possibly but quite probably resided in nucleic acid, the substance Miescher discovered at about the time Mendel was setting down the rules of heredity.

Scientists were still groping at chromosomes and genes as with heavy gloves and poor eyesight. Chromosomes are tiny, and each submicroscopic blob may contain *thousands* of genes! Clever researchers found that chromosomes of the Mediterranean fruit fly are relatively large; under the best microscopes they could faintly see light and dark bands that might be the genes themselves.

In the early 1940's Beadle and Tatum investigated the genes of a bread mold and learned many things about how the genes controlled cell chemistry. And in 1944 a trio of workers headed by Oswald Avery at Rockefeller Institute proved in experiments with the virus that causes pneumonia that deoxyribonucleic acid, or DNA, carried information to cells. Importantly they showed that DNA from *dead* cells could move to living cells and still bring their blueprint that told the cells what to do.

All this, remember, had been accomplished without anyone yet having seen an actual gene. Scientists knew where the culprit was and what it did; what it looked like and how it performed had to be arrived at by scientifically educated guesswork.

Among those who speculated was Linus Pauling, and his hunch was that DNA must have a helical, or corkscrew, structure. With the coming of the electron microscope, molecules slowly began to reveal their shapes. In 1952 Maurice Wilkins of Kings College in London, using X-ray diffraction techniques, looked at a DNA molecule and knew that Pauling was right, the shape was definitely helical. Then in 1953 James Watson and Francis Crick of Cambridge made a detailed diagram of DNA and showed that Pauling's prediction had been *half* right.

The giant molecule was a *double* helix, like two corkscrews intertwined in a fantastically delicate, springlike structure. In a prophetic way he had not intended, Sir Richard Burton—the earlier one—described the secret of life in a poem written a century ago:

> *Life is a ladder infinite-stepped*
> *That hides its rungs from human eyes.*

The twisted strands of DNA were indeed infinite-stepped ladders, with rungs far too small to be seen by human eyes! As an indication of the complexity of the gene, a molecule of myoglobin is composed of 2,600 atoms. The DNA molecule contains hundreds of thousands of atoms.

Pinning down DNA was much like discovering the atom. The job was by no means finished, in fact it seemed to have only begun. Besides DNA, there was another nucleic acid in the cell. This was ribonucleic acid, or RNA. Almost immediately it was found that there are several types of RNA, to further confuse the picture. Slowly it was learned that the main types are "transfer" and "messenger" RNA that carry the blueprint, or a copy of it, from gene to tissue. Also isolated was an odd DNA type with only a single strand, or helix, instead of the usual two. But then it would have been disillusioning to find the basis for life too simple a thing.

By 1961 scientists at the Fifth International Congress on Biochemistry held in Moscow heard results of experiments with artificial messenger RNA and attempts at breaking the DNA "code." There are four letters in the nucleic "alphabet," and they are used in groups of three to spell out the words of instruction for production of the 20 amino acids which in long chains form the needed protein types in the cells.

Arthur Kornberg shared a Nobel Prize for synthesizing DNA in 1959 and his product almost—but not quite—duplicated the real thing. Gerhard Schramm at the Max Planck Institute in Germany synthesized nucleic acid in late 1962. More recently Klaus Hoffman at the University of Pittsburgh synthesized an enzyme called nuclease.

Progress toward knowledge about genetics, then, began at a leisurely walk. Today we are racing toward an answer that is imminent, or at least around a not-too-remote corner. Some scientists speak of artificial DNA that will match the original living material. Others are more cautious. Meanwhile, man has at least learned much about himself and his genetic structure.

Every living thing begins as a single cell. The amoeba remains a single cell; man develops into an adult with some 60 *trillion* cells! The cell's knowledge of *how* to grow, *where* to grow, and *when* to grow is the miracle of life. The egg cell grows into more cells simply by dividing. It would seem a fantastically long way from 1 cell to 60 trillion, yet "binary fission," as the process of cell-splitting is called, accomplishes this increase in less than fifty divisions. But while getting 60 trillion cells from one original is simple enough arithmetically, biologically it is quite another story. That is where the miracle of DNA comes in.

The cell, the building block of life, is a tiny sphere of liquid encased in membrane and with a nucleus at its center. The chromosomes with their many genes are quite naturally found in this nucleus, well-protected by the surrounding fluid of the cell. By now we have some concept of the infinitesimal size of the DNA blueprint we are talking about. The cell is microscopic, the nucleus is only a small part of it. Our original cell starts with 46 chromosomes, and it is these amazing and tiny bits of matter that determine whether we will be male or female, fair or dark, short or tall, blue-eyed or brown-eyed, plus all the other characteristics that make us individuals. It is unbelievable that only 46 "instructions" could map out all these characteristics in a human, so it is not too great a surprise to learn that the chromosome itself is composed of many genes, perhaps about 3,000 in humans. Thus there are some 150,000 genes in our bodies.

As we saw earlier, the gene turns out to be a "giant" molecule, although this term is only relative and apt to be misleading. At any rate, our gene consists of many small molecules, each composed of still more thousands of atoms, linked together in the double helix discovered by Wilkins, Crick, and Watson. This coil is called a "polypeptide" chain since it is made up of many peptides of sugar and phosphate. Composed of only twenty amino acids, the chain can nevertheless be formed in any of thousands of trillions of combinations!

The two strands of the helix are interconnected at intervals by hydrogen bonds between bases labeled A, C, T, and G for their chemical names of adenine, cytosine, thymine, and guanine. A, C, T, and G are the letters of the "genetic code."

It is the job of the genes to make enzymes, the fluids that grow protein out of the raw material available in body cells, and it is the coded series of A, C, T, and G hydrogen bonds, or "nucleotides" that makes the proper enzyme.

The double helix of polypeptides and nucleotides are actually "complementary" coils—sort of mirror images. Where one coil has an A base, the opposite coil has an interlocking T base that is compatible with the A. C and G bases are similarly complementary. The coils thus fit together like a three-dimensional jigsaw puzzle. At the instant of cell division the double coils separate at the bonds, and shortly thereafter each creates a new and perfectly matching helix partner of the raw material floating around it. This is how the blueprint is passed on from the original egg cell to each successive cell in our bodies so that the miraculous "word" of life is everywhere in us from the top of our head to the tips of our toenails. Each cell has an exact carbon copy of the original DNA blueprint, and yet each cell also "differentiates" itself through some magical dropping out of the power of certain genes at exactly the right time. In other words, when our nose is complete it does not continue to grow longer, and the cells that sprouted from our legs to become feet and then branched out into toes do not again divide. This property of differentiation increases in higher life forms and is the reason man cannot grow a new finger if he loses one, even though the lizard has this amazing capability. The lizard's cell differentiation has not progressed to the point of man's. You can't have everything.

Once scientists learned the letters of the genetic alphabet they began to wonder about the words themselves. With four letters it was obvious that a single letter could not form a word, since to describe the twenty amino acids in the original DNA molecule would take five times the four letters available. Two-letter words would not suffice either, since four letters yield only sixteen different two-letter combinations. Thus it was decided that the genetic code must be spelled out in three-letter words, with from one hundred to one thousand of those words forming a gene. There are sixty-four combinations of three letters, enough for the total of amino acids needed plus a good surplus to be on the safe side. Perhaps some of the additional words mean "stop building," "starting building," and so on. Some of them mean the same as other words, and the genetic code is often called a "degenerate" code. This harsh-sounding description simply means that two or more words mean the same thing. English is degenerate by this standard, since "boy" and "lad" both mean young male.

Amazingly, all of life seems to speak the same language; a word in the code means the same thing to man's cells as it does to those of a gnat. This idea is advanced by the knowledge that when a virus invades a foreign cell it creates duplicate viruses by using its DNA blueprint on the cell's raw materials.

This is not to say, of course, that the DNA code is the same in all living things. Experiments at Carnegie Institution demonstrate that human DNA combines with that from rhesus monkeys almost as strongly as with other human DNA, not so strongly with mouse DNA, weakly with salmon, and almost not at all with that from bacteria. Such compatibility would seem to bear out evolutionary theory, incidentally.

Scientists peering at a tiny virus with electron microscopes noted that the length of the DNA blueprint the virus injected into the cell to create dozens more of the same virus was 150 times the diameter of the virus itself. Human DNA is far more complex. One estimate is that there are perhaps *five lineal feet* of coded instructions, or "tape" in the nucleus of a single cell. Furthermore, the information contained in this tape would fill 1,000 volumes of the Encyclopaedia Britannica with three-letter words of instructions!

Since preservation of the original DNA code of life is vital if the world of living things is not to turn into a freak circus, the DNA molecule itself stays in the cell nucleus. We have a parallel situation in our standards laboratories, where meter rods are kept under glass and at precise temperatures, used only to check the working measuring instruments against. In genetics, it is RNA that carries a faithful copy of the DNA "standard" out into the cell to do the actual construction work.

The Tinkerers

There is understandably great interest among scientists in this race to discover the secret of life, an interest that increases as researchers close in toward final answers. Many things are hastening progress—things like the electron microscope, high-speed computers, studies of disease, developments in drugs and radiation, and so on. The prime mover, however, is man's own instinctive curiosity.

The potential inherent in the secret of life is tremendous. If man can create life, he can also change life. It is hoped that DNA will unlock the secrets of cancer and let man wipe out this cruel disease. The tragedies of malformed babies and other evidences of nature running wild may be avoided. Heart trouble may be thwarted, and man may learn to understand that most terrible of all diseases—mental illness. Perhaps through DNA we can achieve true happiness for everyone. Our food is a life form, and DNA may help us produce more and better food for the growing population of the world and also the astronauts who will colonize other planets.

We may learn the secret of aging and how to foil this seeming shortcoming of life; perhaps man has immortality in his grasp. If so, the wildest imaginings of the science-fiction writer will be not only possible but probable.

Just how gene-tinkering, or genetic engineering, is to be accomplished is a question. Technicians are not yet assembling genetic material with tweezers; the synthesis from raw materials so far has been on a gross scale. Perhaps it may be necessary to start with nature's product and alter it with drugs or possibly with ionizing radiation. The task will be difficult and of colossal magnitude, but this is not deterring workers. The difficulty, instead, seems to add to the challenge and serve as a goad toward progress.

A promising approach to the new genetics is that of quantum mechanics. Ever since the functions of the gene became fuzzily apparent, man has tried to reconcile the paradox of heredity and mutation. It is the duty of the hereditary mechanism of the gene to guarantee that man produces human babies and monkeys give rise to little monkeys; nature goes to fantastic ends to guard against any mixing of species. Yet if evolution is to take place there must be change, there must be mutations. Nature must provide for this selective upgrading process but just how has been a great mystery.

In the 1930's M. Delbruck pointed out that there were interesting similarities in the theory of quantum mechanics advanced by Planck and the fundamental theory of heredity. Quantum mechanics is based on the idea of molecules at various states or levels of energy, and the ability to move from one state to another by the "quantum jump" method. Similarly, Delbruck argued, the giant molecule of the gene could move from its normally stable state to another state; a state that would give rise to a different set of genetic instructions.

In the 1940's when Watson and Crick had evolved the true picture of the gene as a giant molecule they also hypothesized that the spontaneous changes in structure, or mutations, arose when the nucleotide base occurred in one of its less likely forms.

Extending this idea, Swedish scientist Per-Olev Lowdin, working at the University of Florida, believes that the quantum jump does take place, and that a proton moves from one side of the helix of the gene to the other. The process, he points out, is similar to the tunneling effect observed in solid state physics and applied to produce the tunnel diode so dear to the heart of the electronics engineer.

Lowdin believes that these spontaneous changes of state are responsible for evolutionary changes, and also for such cell anomalies as cancer. Further, he thinks they are the clue to aging itself. Spontaneous mutations continue to occur and over a period of time the total effect is sufficient to cause aging, and the tumors that often go with old age.

In the artificially built man, if these mutations were prevented or controlled, there might be no aging and no cancer or other tumorous growths. Nature had to take the bad along with the good to achieve new species. The "human engineer" accomplishes with his basic blueprint a stable being that will not produce mutations within itself that lead to cancer and death from old age. Here, then, would be the secret not only of life, but of eternal life, the Fountain of Youth Ponce de Leon searched for in vain in this same Florida where Lowdin is doing his research.

The Mystery of Aging

The greatest desire of men is for eternal youth. From Merlin down to Cagliostro, Brown-Sequard, and Voronoff, charlatans and scientists have pursued the same dream and suffered the same defeat. No one has discovered the supreme secret. Meanwhile, our need for it is becoming more and more urgent.

Until quite recently, aging was similar to the weather in that everybody deplored it but nobody could do anything about it. The men referred to tried, as did others like Ponce de Leon with his wishful searching for a fountain that would give him eternal youth. But it was Dr. Alexis Carrel, quoted above, who made the first steps toward the halting of aging, the process that makes old men of us all.

A cell colony [Carrel said] begins to record time as soon as its waste products are allowed to stagnate and thus alter its surroundings. . . . The rate of accumulation of the waste products in the medium, and the nature of these products, determine the characteristics and the duration of the tissues. When the composition of the medium is maintained constant, the cell colonies remain indefinitely in the same state of activity. . . . Colonies from a heart fragment removed in January, 1912, from a chick embryo, are growing as actively today as twenty-three years ago. In fact, they are immortal.

Despite his "immortal" chicken heart, Carrel was pessimistic on the possibility of immortal man:

Like physical time, physiological time is irreversible. In fact, it is as irreversible as the processes responsible for its existence. In the higher animals, duration never changes its direction. However, in hibernating mammals, it becomes partly suspended. In a dried rotifer, its flow comes to a complete standstill. The organic rhythm of cold-blooded animals accelerates when their environment becomes warmer. . . .

But in using such simple procedures, it is not possible to induce in men any profound change of the tissues. The rhythm of physiological time is not modifiable except by interference with certain fundamental processes and their mode of association. We cannot retard senescence or reverse its direction, unless we know the nature of the mechanisms which are the substratum of duration. . . .

In recent years interest in the problem of aging has heightened, perhaps because there are more older people. By the 1950's there was increasing research into the problem of aging, backed in large part by the National Institutes of Health. By 1961 this branch of government research was spending more than $30 million a year on hundreds of projects. Some of the scientists involved go along generally with Carrel's theory of waste product accumulation slowly stifling the cells and causing aging and death. But there are many other theories, ranging from that of "mistakes" made by the genes over a period of time, to changes wrought by ionizing radiation (interestingly, such radiation in some life forms *increases* life span dramatically!) and the collection of pigments in the cells and the effects of collagen bonds between cells.

Russia's Zh. A. Medvedev is among those who continue to point out that mortality of individuals is necessary for evolution to take place, and that although each of us individually dies the species is continuous back to the dawn of time and if nature has its way will continue in the future. Medvedev suggests that aging thus be considered as a genetically built-in weakening of the control of reproduction of all structures.

Immortality will never occur in nature, except as rocks and other formations are practically immortal. But man in the laboratory seems bent on finding the key to everlasting life for himself, despite any inherent dangers in such an endeavor. We have touched on the ideas of euthenics and the more drastic glandular transplants and implants of artificial organs in an effort to prolong life. The ultimate in long-lived man may be developed by tampering with a genetic structure that seems designed to produce old age.

Calculated Risk

Whether used to create man, or to make him immortal, the secrets of life can be a danger, perhaps greater than the secrets of death our weapons makers have learned. Some scientists warn that man may create artificial life so virulent it will supersede him just as the present forms of life battled and bested other candidates in the dim past of our planet. Some religions deplore attempts at the creation of life in the laboratory, believing that man is meddling where he has no business.

To balance this understandable concern it is well to remember that much of the progress made in the struggle toward learning life's secret has come from work with the virus diseases that threaten to wipe man out. Surely we could not be destined to stand idly by and be exterminated by plagues of disease. Mankind, motivated by a force we may never understand even with the secret of life unlocked and displayed before us in bright light, seeks to keep alive and improving. Despite the setbacks of wars and inventions that threaten destruction, man remains alive, healthy and even improving if we look at the overall picture. We do what we must; what is right must prevail.

Putting a timetable on further progress toward artificial life is difficult. Today, after scarcely more than a century of actual work toward the goal, man—who is millions of years old—stands in the doorway to tremendous change. At any moment he may take the step that carries him through and to the other side. How long that moment will really be no one knows.

As this is written, two researchers have synthesized DNA and successfully changed the hereditary characteristics of bacteria. Bacteria are not men, of course, and so the race of laboratory supermen heralded in news headlines is still some distance off. However, science knows that it is only a matter of degree, now that the basic principle has been demonstrated.

Also accomplished is the creation of the base adenine, one of the four nucleotides that make up the genetic alphabet, under conditions man thinks existed on earth in the days before there was life.

In the laboratory an electron beam was passed through a mixture of methane, ammonia, and water, material thought to have existed in "pre-biotic" ages. Adenine was produced and isolated. Even though none of the other three nucleotides (cytosine, guanine, and thymine) were produced, the researchers point out that of the four adenine has the greatest radiation resistance and stability and thus is most likely to survive. Earlier experiments with electricity and the methane-ammonia-water mixture produced amino acids a decade ago. Thus science is not only finding the key to life, but learning how it began on earth ages ago.

While part of the genetic fraternity is optimistic as to man's future in controlling his genetic structure, there are also those who counsel caution and common sense. Among these is T. M. Sonneborn. Agreeing that all things are possible, he feels that it is very unlikely that man will in the near future be able to tinker with his genes artificially to produce a race of supermen. This is simply because nature has done such a fantastically good job of protecting the process of heredity. The laws of probability and the sheer weight of large numbers makes human engineering seem a hopeless task, Sonneborn says. We have seen that although there are just 20 amino acids involved in the spiral of the gene, rearrangements of these randomly in 1,000 sites lead to 10^{600}

different genes! Any engineering man does on future men at a genetic level must be of a very simplified nature.

Evolution itself has evolved, until it is a fantastically effective method of policing nature's output. For example, Dr. John Frederick Spalding of the University of California's Los Alamos Scientific Laboratory has dosed 32 successive generations of rats with radiation, with surprising results. Genetic damage was weeded out through death, and more offspring were produced as if to counteract for these deaths. A few cases of hydrocephalus turned up, but there was also a baldness-producing mutation in the nonradiated control group. The 32 generations are equivalent to about 900 years of human life, and Dr. Spalding feels that the race is not likely to eliminate itself through genetic damage.

In summing up, Sonneborn says he thinks the possibility of genetic engineering in man seems very far away indeed. However, the possibility of creating life in any form seemed even farther away, only a short time ago.

On the opposite side, one writer-scientist estimates that by the turn of the century the molecular biologist may well have at his disposal the ability to understand mankind sufficiently well to guarantee his future, protecting it against the dangers from other sources, and just as importantly, from man himself.

Granting that the scientist's "Book of Genesis" may differ from that in the Bible, some writers have pointed out that such a spontaneous generation of life is not necessarily incompatible with that of supernatural creation. As scientists themselves point out, great faith is required for the acceptance of either view.

15 *Morality of the Cyborg*

After days and nights of incredible labor and fatigue, I succeeded in discovering the cause of generation and life; nay, more, I became myself capable of bestowing animation upon lifeless matter.

When I found so astonishing a power placed within my hands I hesitated a long time concerning the manner in which I should employ it.

> Mary Shelley
> *Frankenstein*
> 1818

In the preceding chapters we have glimpsed a development in man called the cyborg. From a tree-branch crutch man has progressed to electronic hands and hearts of metal, plastic, and wire. As a participant in his own evolution, he has succeeded in creating *homo machina*, the man-machine, the artificial man. With electronics, mechanics and chemistry he is altering his physical body as well as its output and the result is a sort of "transhuman" being with no counterpart in what we generally consider nature.

This is not to say that superman is at this moment in a phone booth donning his cyborgian electro-chemo-mechanical space suit. The cyberneticist whose task is the creation of cyborgs has his hands full of problems that strain the scientific and technological state of the art. We are not yet "there" and perhaps never will reach an ultimate that we keep moving farther ahead. But there is another problem of the cyborg and what it promises to be: not the mechanical, nuts and bolts, transistor and tunnel diode kind but the moral problem. Granting that man *can* make a superman, does he have the *right* to do so? And if so, how many are to be supermen and at what cost to others? It is well that such problems are beginning to be considered, and that there have already been skirmishes along the ragged line of battle shaping up.

The war between science and theology is almost as old as those institutions, despite the fact that medicine and religion long went hand in hand. Jesus is remembered well as a healer, and long before him there were medicine men, witch doctors, the Egyptian combinations of divine and physician, and Roman medicine with its "goddesses even for the itch." Dr. Joseph Fletcher, in his book, *Morals and Medicine*, mentions humorously that, as late as the generation preceding his, rabbis printed up cards reading "Weddings and circumcisions respectfully solicited."

It was when medicine became scientific enough to shrug off its dependence on religion that the two paths diverged. Even now, however, the two are in most instances within easy hailing distance and it is generally only such questions as birth control that cause great chasms between. As Fletcher points out, some ministers have actually pioneered medical research in the face of great storms of protest and physical reprisal by the populace. For example, Reverend Thomas Thatcher in 1777 published what was the first medical treatise in this country urging quarantine in cases of smallpox. In the next century Cotton and Increase Mather were among the preachers to support Dr. Zabdiel Boyleston in his inoculation experiments. The general public was so incensed that it burned down the hospital at Marblehead in Massachusetts where inoculations were first given.

The word *anthropos* means "one who walks with his face to the heavens." There will always be those who believe that man is not walking but flying in the face of those heavens when he seemingly circumvents nature. These alleged floutings are becoming closer together and bolder with the passage of time. Enough of us already question the wisdom of shooting men at the moon; when it becomes common knowledge that scientists are tinkering with humans by drugging, freezing and otherwise altering their structure and capabilities the outcry will be much louder and broader in scope.

The greatest protest has always been over the idea of man taking the power of life into his own hands via birth control. Although it is easy to see that nature itself "does away" with many potential lives—during the menstrual cycle for example, by miscarriage and abortion, and by limiting the span of years during which conception is possible—it is not as easy to make a case for man's tampering with life. To be sure, if all the potential births *did* occur, the world would be knee deep in people—mostly dead ones. Yet a life prevented by contraception may have flowered into genius or even a savior of the world. This is a moral problem of great magnitude. Yet man seems to be doing the right thing from an overall standpoint with dissemination of devices for contraception, and the newer anti-conception pills. The alternative could be further overpopulation alleviated only by some modest proposal like Swift's or a less modest one by nature itself in which starvation and disease take charge to limit the number of humans "naturally."

Having thus disposed of the moral question of artificially preventing life, we have remaining the question of artificial prolongation of life. There are with us those religious sects that object strenuously to man's intervention in what they consider God's workings and refuse medical aid for those who will die without such aid. Opposed to them, yet perhaps as inconsistent, are those who refuse to countenance euthanasia in any form. The medical profession generally seems bound to go along with the idea that life *must* be prolonged for as long as it is scientifically possible, even if this keeps a miserable hulk of humanity among the living far past the time he is of any usefulness to others or himself and when it would seem humane to spare him further suffering.

There are also those middle-roaders who believe in using every trick in the book to save a life worth saving, and at the same time see the good in letting terminate—or even assisting in the termination of—a life of no value to the individual or society. This would seem an enlightened view, yet it does not completely take care of the problem. Let us consider the use of artificial organs as a case in point.

There are those who want desperately to live, and will do all they can to cling to life. There are also those few who have intentionally damaged or maladjusted the connections to artificial organs keeping them alive and thus ended their lives. Dr. Kolff, who pioneered the use of such artificial organs, asks the question of what the doctor should do when the patient will die of a heart disease unless he is fitted with an artificial heart. Is not such an "artificial" life preferable to a "natural" death? Or is it a perversion of God's plan, which must of necessity include those seemingly pointless sacrifices of life that are actually significant and of great importance in the scheme of things?

Kolff also mentions the case of a patient kept alive by frequent visits to the hospital where he had access to an artificial kidney. However, his wife "could not stand the strain" and finally took him to a hospital where such treatment was not available. Was the woman right? Was justice done, or a murder committed? Shaw, in *The Doctor's Dilemma,* asks the question of who is worth saving. The medical practitioner cannot hope to save all, and must at times make such a decision. He has taken on the responsibilities of God, it would seem.

More recently this responsibility is being faced continually by the board in Seattle that screens candidates for the pitifully few artificial kidneys available in the hospital. Of fifty hopefuls, only one can be accepted. Those over forty-five, for example, and children under twelve, are "automatically" excluded. Heartless? Consider the mental anguish not only of those turned down, but of the anonymous men and women who serve on the board and whose only recompense may be just this agony of decision. The Seattle board and its problems brings up an even bigger problem growing out of the artificial-kidney technique. Granted that we can keep alive people who would otherwise die without artificial parts, we can do this at a great cost in money and in the time and efforts of other people. As this condition continues and expands, do we face a world in which half of us are doomed to minister to the weaker half? The alternative would seem cruelly inhumane, of course. Considering that in 1963 Americans spent $33 billions for medical care, it might be hoped that cyborg techniques would actually *save* us money.

It was Martin Luther who said that no malady comes from God. Taking this view, the scientist would seem to have a clear conscience in working to destroy the virus infections that prey on man and to replace a diseased kidney or heart with another, even though it is made of metal and plastics.

Conceivably the replacement of human hearts and kidneys and perhaps other organs could extend the lives of the persons concerned. What will be the result of changing the span from the traditional three score and ten? What effect will this have on religion, on education, on government? Will not the insurance business be affected profoundly, to say nothing of the undertaking profession and perhaps the medical profession as well?

Overpopulation will be aggravated by longevity, and to alleviate it man must further curb his procreation. As noted earlier, much work is being done on the problem of aging; if research resulted in a drug that could slow the aging process man might live far longer than the extra years a new heart and other organs would give him.

Employment practices would need drastic revision as the population's average age increased. Or perhaps there will be little work for humans to do anyhow, and the problem will be what to do with more leisure time.

Although Darwin's paper on evolution was subtitled "The Descent of Man," evolution seems to be ascent rather than descent, working toward higher types. The secondary, or participant evolution man has overlaid onto genetic evolution has the same direction—toward the more complex, the more sophisticated. There is much talk of "the good old days" but few scientists are working in that direction. Generally it is agreed that the best thing about those fabled times is that we were younger then. What we seem to be shooting for rather than the simple, pastoral life is one filled with ever more creature comforts, interesting things to do and more youth and vigor with which to enjoy them. The "retirement towns" springing up about the country are an example of this. Far from retirement, many of them feature a bang-bang timetable of scheduled fun and games that run the senior citizens ragged.

It is interesting to recall the legendary ages of those patriarchs in Genesis whose lives spanned ten times our own. Man may be heading in the direction of full circle and his descendants may be living such fabled ages in a few generations. Fascinating as such a prospect of immortality or something close to it would be, it should be remembered that immortality carries the seeds of an end to evolution. All new forms are based on earlier forms they evolved from; all new growth stems from the death of earlier life.

Such would seem to be the case in our own experience. Nature sought to evolve living things from the amoeba to man. If all the early tries were alive today chaos and confusion would be the order. Man dies to make room for a next, and hopefully better, generation. If he tosses in the monkey wrench in the form of immortality there will be the end of progress. From the genetic standpoint, this is quite true. But we have seen that to all intents participant evolution in humans has superseded or overridden genetic evolution.

Even the immortal human, with no progeny, could effect changes in his kind. A world with time no longer a factor is an interesting situation to consider, and perhaps the greatest hazard of all would be sheer boredom that would kill us off. Thus the fear of evolution's end in immortality no longer seems to apply.

Given long life, perhaps there would be no great need to create artificial life, but man being what he is will surely continue with laboratory copies of living things. Assuming success, what then? What status would this new, artificial human have in the eyes of the law, his fellow man, his minister? How would it affect him to know that he was different in this important respect from those around him? This problem has been treated in science fiction for years, but no definite solutions have been reached.

Will supermen compete with ordinary mortals? Will the government control their production and participate in their design? Will cyborgs nevertheless take over the running of nations and the world?

The morality of the cyborg concept is of course a problem of the future. But that future begins tomorrow.

16 *The Cyborg's Future*

I suppose one could call a man in an iron lung a Cyborg, but the concept has far wider implications than this. One day we may be able to enter into temporary unions with any sufficiently sophisticated machines, thus being able not merely to control but to become a spaceship or a submarine or a TV network. This would give far more than purely intellectual satisfaction; the thrill that can be obtained from driving a racing car or flying an airplane may be only a pale ghost of the excitement our great-grandchildren may know, when the individual human consciousness is free to roam at will from machine to machine, through all the reaches of sea and sky and space.

But how long will this partnership last? Can the synthesis of man and machine ever be stable, or will the purely organic component become such a hindrance that it has to be discarded? If this eventually happens—and I have tried to give reasons why it must—we have nothing to regret, and certainly nothing to fear.

Arthur C. Clarke
Profiles of the Future
Harper, 1963.

In the preceding chapters we have been introduced to the combination man-machine in a broad spectrum of types ranging from a woman with glasses to a man with a pneumatic arm, from a child with a reconstructed ear or nose to an adult with an electronic pacemaker triggering the pulsations of his heart or governing his blood pressure. As yet there are no artificial supermen among us, although drugs have possibly boosted the capability of some athletes above the natural norm. We have not yet been relegated into second-class citizenry by a new breed of half-men, half-machines. The cyborg today is an interesting prelude.

To recapitulate, there are roughly two fields open to the cyborg. The first and more obvious is the "medical" cyborg, the man-machine in whom an electronic heart or plastic kidney results in a more lasting and trouble-free being. The second is the cyborg tailored for an environment different from the natural conditions found on earth. The space cyborg, for example for either outer or inner space: A man requiring a fraction of the "fuel" normal men need; capable of suspended animation at will and for as long a period as necessary; immune to radiation damage; and designed so that weightlessness is not a detriment. Or, for the space beneath our seas, a cyborg that breathes water, can withstand enormous pressures and cold temperatures, and can communicate in the watery medium, perhaps ultrasonically as do his friends the porpoises.

If something is possible, and if there is some need of it, then it most probably will be developed. Is replacement of many body parts possible? Yes. Is it desirable? Yes, for reasons like prolonging life, and making life pleasanter while it is lived. Mere prolongation of life is assurance of the coming of cyborgs of this type. Men would give their souls for eternal life, according to fiction. If we examine our own minds, we may decide that the fictional view is solidly based on fact. Not if we are in an agony of old age, but if life can be kept rewarding and painfree, who then wants to die? Nature itself has given us an all-powerful drive toward self-preservation. If we can keep ourselves alive and healthy beyond the normal three score and ten, we are likely to do so even if we have to secure the necessary drugs, organs or whatever else is required on the black market or in other illegal fashion.

Men climb mountains because they are there, and journey into the vacuum of space where there is nothing. Man is curious by nature, and trying to bottle up this inner drive is as futile as capping a volcano. Who is to say that curiosity is not a prime mover in man's destiny? Because he has this quality in spades might it not be important in his development? So man will journey to the stars. If he cannot do this in his present form, he will change his form so that he can make the trip.

The cyborg, then, is here to stay and to multiply in numbers and increasingly evolve beyond natural man. No amount of moral censure or governmental restriction can long stifle the drive back of the cyborg. What can we do about it? The old saying goes "if you can't beat 'em, join 'em." This would seem to apply in the case of the artificial man.

Atomic power was long a subject only for science fiction. When it became a fact it changed life in many important ways for all of us. The same was true of spaceflight and the electronic computer, and to lesser extent such other developments as communications satellites, the laser and so on. How much more important is a change that affects man so intimately that it becomes part of him! We should be aware of what is happening. We should know the good that such a development can do, and we should know too the dangers inherent in the cyborg. Sterile cyborgs could wipe out the population. Immortality could lead to horrible overcrowding of the planet. Creation of life in the laboratory may yield forms hostile to natural man, and longevity cause many of our time-honored institutions to crash down around our electronic-ultrasonic ears. Cyborgs may wage war on natural men, or governments resort to cyborgian trickery to control the population like well-regulated robots.

We are witnessing the prelude, playing a part in it, some of us. When will the main show take place?

Scientist Olaf Stapledon considered the four ways in which a superbrain could be created: first by selective breeding, second by manipulation of hereditary factors in laboratory-cultivated germ cells, third by manipulation of fertilized ovum cultivated in the laboratory, and fourth by manipulation of a growing body. Millions of years hence, superbrain creators in Stapledon's fictional history of the future titled *Last and First Men* carefully selected a human ovum, fertilized it in the laboratory and then largely reorganized it by artificial means.

In embryo, the body and lower organs of the creature were inhibited in growth, while the cerebral hemispheres were stimulated. The result was a 12-foot brain with 6-fingered hands. The brain's heart, lungs and other organs were electric or mechanical. Its sensory equipment was a blend of the natural and the artificial.

This first superbrain died after four years, suffering understandably from mental derangement brought on by its brain weight and the failure of chemical regulation of its blood supply. However, after 400 years of research, a new brain 40 feet in diameter was incubated for a period of eight years while it filled a huge "brain room." At age fifty it was a bright adolescent. At sixty it had learned all that man could teach it. Curiosity was its main characteristic, and Stapledon described the superbrain as a "huge bump of curiosity equipped with the most cunning hands."

These "fourth men" took over the world by building 10,000 of themselves, linked by radio and using humans as slaves to tend them. In time they gave way to a new race of "fifth men" who were more nearly human. From here on Stapledon, writing as though getting paid by the year, rambles on through many successive races of men and another two billion years of evolution. His superbrain ideas contain some scientific underpinning, and much accurate prediction, but the book in total reads more like the old "bug-eyed-monster" science fiction magazines. And the timetable to cyborgian superbeings is incredible.

J. D. Bernal, writing at the time Stapledon did, produced a much more realistic book in *The World, The Flesh and The Devil*. Evolution, Bernal felt, is itself evolutionary. Natural man, the product of evolution to this point, is now a dead end. Mechanized man, a break in organic evolution, is actually in the true tradition of further evolution.

This break is more imminent than suggested in Stapledon's book, Bernal hints. "Sooner or later," he says, "some eminent physiologist will break his neck or find his body cells worn out." His choice is to abandon his body or die. But only a Brahmin philosopher could care to live as an isolated brain. In the early stages of such a metamorphosis, this artificial, substitute body would be at a disadvantage compared with normal man, yet surely better than being dead.

Not just self-preservation, but need to adapt quickly to a rapidly changing man-made environment will press for more mechanization of man. Bernal saw the limbs of civilized workers as mere parasites, demanding 90 percent of the body's energy of food, plus blackmail in the form of needed exercise. On the other hand, the increasing complexity of man's existence challenges his mental capacity to deal with it. Much improved sensory and motor organization is required.

Bernal envisaged a fairly normal early life as suggested by J. B. S. Haldane: Birth in an "ectogenetic factory" assembly line, 60 to 120 years of unspecialized existence in normal human form, the years filled with lovemaking, poetry, dancing, and the like, then the important transformation by surgical and mechanical means into specialized man. Bernal's proposed changes are not as drastic as those resulting in Stapledon's superbeings, but still not calculated to comfort those fearful of new forms.

The final product would perhaps be a short metallic cylinder enclosing a human brain cushioned in fluid. An artificial heart-lung machine and digestive system would connect to this cylinder. Eyes and ears would be augmented with powerful optics and also radio communication. Motor organs would provide locomotion and manipulation. Physically the creature might be rather crustacean in appearance, with a single extremity doubling as mouth, tongue, and hands.

"If a method has been found of connecting a nerve ending in a brain directly with an electrical reactor," Bernal says (and it has, of course), "then the way is open for connecting it with a brain of another person. Telepathic communication would lead to perfect thought transfer for the first time, and a meeting of the minds be more than a figure of speech. We would be one in a new kind of immortality, and sense organs would be less and less attached to bodies themselves. There would develop an intellect of the whole earth, and even of distant stars."

Having thought about these mechanized men of the future at great length, Bernal asked the pointed question, "If man is to develop something new, is all humanity going to share it or only a part of it?" This is no new problem, as Bernal suggests in his answers: "We shall have the very same reactionaries at all periods warning us to remain in the natural and primitive state of humanity, which is normally the last stage but one in their cultural history."

Will the cyborg win, or will reaction prevail? Or will a dimorphism exist? Bernal suggests that there may be two groups, with the new breed departing earth for an existence in space, leaving that planet with the "humanists" as a sort of zoo unaware.

Bernal shrinks the time scale from 40 million years to something in the foreseeable future. Present writers are shrinking the "foreseeable future." In 1963, writer-scientist Arthur C. Clarke in his book, *Profiles of the Future*, suggested a timetable for future developments and placed cyborgs in 1990.

This is still a comfortable quarter of a century away, of course. And Clarke may be overly optimistic—or pessimistic, as the case may turn out to be. Even if it is 2000 or 2050, however, the cyborg he refers to is far more sophisticated than the modest "augmented men" suggested in this book. In Clarke's view, the cyborg may well be a transitional type leading to the all-machine being that will eventually think man off the face of the earth.

Perhaps discussion of when the cyborg will hold sway is mere quibbling. Whether or not it will seems already established, and that is the main point. As Bernal succinctly put it, the future was once entirely up to fate, but now our desire affects it.

It is comforting to know that we have an ace in the hole. Barring some genetic magic not foreseen by scientists, all man's dabbling at creating superman will not change the basic product very much. Nature seems to have had an uneasy inkling of what might lie ahead when nosy man began to poke and pry at himself and has made it fantastically difficult to upset the majestic ordering of the human gene. If the cyborgian world should crash down upon us, homo sapiens will prevail. Life will revert to human form again for generations until curiosity can regroup for another cyborg leap ahead.

Index

Aging, study of, 44, 185–187
Air Force School of Medicine San Antonio, 147
School of Aviation Medicine, Brooks Air Force Base, 126
America, 169, 170
American Society for Artificial Internal Organs (ASAIO), 75, 87–90
Amputees, 25, 38, 67–68, 139
Aortas, artificial, 80–81
Arms, artificial, 25, 66, 70
Army cyborgs, 144–145
Army, *see* U.S. Army
Arteries, 26, 80–81, 86
Astronauts, 109–110, 116, 150, 156
Avery, Oswald, 178

Babies, test-tube, 165–166, 167–171
Bacteria and genes, 188
Balance center, 121
Barker, Carl, 81–82
Baropacers, 82–83
Barrett, William, 20
Basmajian, John V., 111
Batteries and implants, 82, 83
Berger rhythm, 97–98
Bernal, J. D., quoted, 22, 93, 100, 117, 146–147, 200–202
Biobattery, 114
Bioelectrogenesis, 115, 116
Bionics, 12, 106, 139–141
defined, 41
Biopower, 114–117
Biotechnology Laboratory, USLA, 62

Birmingham, 80
Birth, control of, 125, 164, 192, 194
defects, 16, 61
Blood, 31–32, 81–85, 100
Bones and metallic repairing, 26–28
Brain, 91–104
artificial, 101–104
electronic stimulation of (ESB), 98–99
and evolution, 93
fictional superbrain, 199–200
operation of, 54–55
and space flight, 150
surgery of, 94–96
waves, 96–100
Brave New World, 173
Breathing
in space flight, 150
water, 142, 155

Cancer, 58, 75, 77, 79–80
eliminating, 175, 183, 185
Čapek, Karel, 157, 158
Carrel, Alexis, 32, 33–34, 44, 78–79
chicken-heart experiment, 33, 185
Man the Unknown, quoted, 46–47, 130–131, 158–159, 185–186
Case Institute of Technology, 113
Cell
and DNA, 180–183
largest human, 176
matching patient and donor, 73
Chicken heart, 33, 185
Cineplasty, 25
Clarke, Arthur C., 197, 202
Cleveland Metropolitan General Hospital, 92

Cleveland Clinic, 83, 84
Clynes, Manfred, quoted, 9, 12, 15, 147–153
Code, genetic, 180–183
Colorado Medical Center, University of, 77
Computers and brain, 101, 103
Contini, Dr. Renato, 144
Contraception, 125, 164, 192, 194
Cora, 102
Cornea grafts, 26, 43, 90
Cornell Aeronautical Laboratories, 144
Crick, Francis, 178, 180, 184
Cryogenics, 128
Cryobiology, 132, 139
Cryosurgery, 133–134
Cybernetics, 37, 139
Cyborg, defined, 9, 12–14
and drugs, 123–124, 149–152
future of, 197–202
"medical," 198
military, 137–145
morality of, 190–196
for other environments, 198
primitive, 19
spacemen, 18, 147–157
"Cyborgs and Space," 9

Darwin, 17, 165, 176
Deformity, and Thalidomide, 124–125
Demikhov, 78
Denver, 77
Deoxyribonucleic acid (DNA), 44, 172, 175, 178
defined, 43, 178
genetic code, 180–183
Differentiation, cell, 161, 180–183
Disease, avoiding through DNA, 175, 183, 185

Doctors and prolonging life, 192–194
Donovan's Brain, 91, 92
Drugs, 80, 119–120, 130
and alteration of man, 118–127
automatic dispenser, 123–124
and space flight, 149, 150, 151, 152
"Drugs, Space and Cybernetics: Evolution to Cyborgs," 147

Ears, 46, 72, 151
Edwards, Dr. W. Sterling, 80
Elbow, electric, 67
Electricity and brain, 96–100
Electromyography and government, 139
Electronics and man, 20, 40
ESB, 98–99
Embryo, test-tube, 43, 168–170
Emotions and space flight, 152
Energizers, psychic, 120–121
Engineering, genetic, 44, 183–185, 188–189
Enzymes, 175, 181
Ethics and artificial organs, 75, 90
Ettinger, Robert C. W., 128–129, 134, 135, 136
Eugenics, 165–166
Euthanasia, 192
Evolution, 9–11
participant, 14–15, 37, 147, 162, 194
Eye, corneal graft, 26, 43, 90
improvements on, 58
operation of, 55–56
Eyelids and myoelectric hand, 113

Fletcher, Dr. Joseph, 191
Flies, research on, 166, 177–178
Food factory, 160
Foot, artificial, 70
Forest Glen Laboratory, 62, 64

Frankenstein, Dr., 34–35, 190
Freedman, Dr. Toby, 155–156
Freezing and immortality, 134–136
Frogmen, 141–142
Fulton, Dr. John F., 95

Galton, Sir Francis, 165–166
Gedda, Professor Luigi, 169
Genes, artificial, 174, 175
bread mold, 178
and DNA, 43, 44, 172, 175, 178, 180–183
mutation of, 124–125, 126
nucleic acid, 43–44
research on, 174–183
General Electric Company, 115, 145
Germans, artificial limbs, 70–71
brain shocks, 96
cineplasty, 25
Gibbon, Dr. John H., 79
Glimcher, Dr. Melvin J., 107–107
Glycerol, 132
Grafts, animal, 33, 42–43
aorta, 80–81
corneal, 26, 43, 90
thyroid, 32
types of, 71–74
Graves, Robert, 106
Gurfinkel, V. S., 69, 108

Hafner, Otto, 66
Haldane, J. B. S., 201
Hallucinogens, 121–123
Halstead, Ward C., 96
Hand, artificial, 65
computer - controlled myoelectric, 113
motivator, 65–66
Russian myoelectric, 107–108
Harvard Medical School, 79, 106
Heart, 76
artificial, 83–84, 193
attacks, reducing, 79
and circulation, 79
diaphragm-muscle, 82
electricity generated around, 40

Heart (*Continued*)
function of, 53
power of, 116–117
transplant, 78
Heart-lung machine, 79–80
Heat and life, 129–130
Helium, breathing, 142
Heuer, Kenneth, 146, 154
Hibernation, 130
Hoffman, Klaus, 179
Hughes Aircraft Company, 143
Huxley, Aldous, 122, 173
Huxley, Julian, 10, 11
Hyperbaria, 153–154
Hypothermia, 44, 128–136
defined, 129
and drugs, 130
and operations, 132–134
and space flight, 149–150, 151, 153

Ideas, "seven ages of," 88–89
Immortality and hypothermia, 134–136
Injector, Rose osmotic, 123–124
Interface, 143

Jacobsen, Dr. Carlyle, 95
Joints, artificial, 71
Jump, quantum, 184
Jupiter, 154

Kamikaze pilot, 138
Kidney, artificial, 39, 84–86, 193
circulatory system, 32
function of, 54
transplanting, 33, 42, 76–77
Kirby, Dr. Charles K., 88, 90
Kline, Dr. Nathan S., quoted, 9, 15, 147–153
Kobrinsky, A. E., 69, 108
Kolff, Dr. Willem, 39, 193
artificial hearts, 83–84
artificial kidney, 84
artificial pancreas, 86, 123
Konecci, Dr. Eugene, 154
Konikoff, J. J., 115
Kornberg, Arthur, 179

Kornbluth, C. S., 159
Krukenberg stump, 25
Kusserow, Dr. B. J., 83

Landauer, Dr. Kenneth S., 65
Last and First Man, 199–200
Lear, John, 106, 107
Legs, artificial, 24, 38–39, 70–71
Leucotomy, 94–96
Levine, Dr. Irving R., 116
Li, C. H., 150
Life, "artificial," 193–194
  beginning of, 188
  reproducing, 162–163, 165–171
Lillehei, Dr. C. Walter, 88
Lima, Dr. Almeida, 95
Limbo, 67–68, 111–113, 137
Limbs, first artificial, 24
  powered, 38–39
  Russian myoelectric, 107–108
Lindbergh, Charles, 33
Lister, Joseph, 27
Liver, transplanted, 42, 77
Lobotomy, crude, 34
  prefrontal, 94–96
London, National Institute for Medical Research, 132
Los Alamos, 189
L'Osservatore Romano, 168, 169
Lowdin, Per-Olev, 184–185
LSD, 122
Lungs, fuel cell for spacemen, 150
  function of, 53–54
  heart-lung machines, 79–80
  transplants, 77
Lyman, Dr. John, 62, 74, 111
  quoted, 60

Machine, human body as, 46–59
Man, adapting to space conditions, 147–156

Man *(Continued)*
  amplifier, bio-controlled, 144
  development of artificial, 38
  as machine, 46–59
  and toolmaking, 11, 22–24
Man the Unknown, 46–47, 130–131, 158–159, 185–186
Mare Island, 62
Massachusetts General Hospital, 106
Massachusetts Institute of Technology, 106
McKibben, Dr. Joseph L., 65
Medawar, P. B., 10
Medvedeo, Zh. A., 186
Melpar, Inc., 159–160
Mendel, Gregor, 43, 175, 176–177
Metabolism and space flight, 149–150, 151, 152
Metals, internal use of, 26–28
Mexico, 63
Miescher, Friedrich, 177
Miller, Dr. James W., 144
Mind changers, 120–121
Mississippi Medical Center, University of, 78
Mobot, 141, 143
Molecule, DNA, 178–183
Moniz, Dr. A. Egaz, 95
Monkey
  brain in laboratory, 92
  and DNA, 182
  glands, 32–33
Morality of cyborg, 190–196
Morals and Medicine, 191
Muller, Dr. Herman J., 166, 171
Muscle boosters, for astronauts, 109–110
  EMG, 140
  tone, on space flight, 150
  training, 110, 111
Muscles, and cineplasty, 25
  generating electricity, 40, 82, 117
  operation of, 51–53

Mutations, 163, 166
  spontaneous, 184–185

NASA and artificial heart, 84
NASA Biotechnology and Human Research Group, 154
Nausea and drugs, 121, 151
Neurophone, 99–100
New Orleans, 77
North American Aviation, 66, 155
Northrop, John, 70
Nose, function of, 56
  replacing, 29–30
Nuclein, 177
Nucleotides, 188

Olds, Dr. James, 152
Organs, artificial, 78–86
  function of vital, 53–54
  and prolonging life, 193–194
  reproductive, 32–33, 54, 78
  transplanting living, 32, 41–43
Oxygen and hyperbaria, 154
Oxygenators, 79

Pacemaker, electronic, 40
  external, 81
  implanted, 82
Pauling, Linus, 178
Pedipulators, 145
Peirce, Dr. E. Converse, II, 135–136
Perfusion, apparatus for, 32
  pump, 33
Petrucci, Dr. Danielle, 168–170
Philco Corporation, 144
Pohl, Frederik, 159
Polio, 24
  arm motivator, 66
  and hand motivator, 65–66
Pope Innocent VIII, 31, 78
Pressure circulation, 32
Profiles of the Future, 197, 202

Prolongation of life, 192–194
and cyborg, 198
Prospect of Immortality, The, 128–129
Prosthetics, defined, 63; 64–71
and the military services, 16, 61–62, 64, 138–139
and rehabilitation, 61–63
Psilocybin, 122

Quantum mechanics, 184
Queen's University, 110–111

Radiation, damage by, 17, 18
and immune reaction, 41, 77
and life span, 186
and mutations, 126, 166
and space flight, 149
Rats and bioelectricity, 115
Reaction, immune, 29
thwarting, 41–42, 73–74, 76, 77
and tissue culture, 161
Rehabilitation of amputees, 61–62
and muscle training, 110
and prosthetics, 61–63
Reproduction and evolution, 162–171
Reynolds, L. W., 115
Ribonucleic acid (RNA), 175, 179, 183
Robots, electronic, 102
mobile, 141, 143
Rock, Dr. John, 167
Rockefeller Institute, 178
Rogers, Edith Nourse, 139
Rose osmotic injector, 123–124
Rostand, Jean, 129, 132, 134
R. U. R., 157, 158
Rhinoplasty, 29–30
Rusk, Dr. Howard A., 62
Russians, and aging, 186
animals breathing water, 142, 155

Russians (*Continued*)
and artificial limbs, 40, 69–70, 107–108
electronic sleep inducer, 98
freezing bats, 132
monkey glands, 32–33, 78
spacemen, 151, 156
stapling arteries, 86
and transplants, 78

Salisbury, Dr. Peter, 86, 87–88
San Francisco, 62, 155
School of Aviation Medicine, Brooks AFB, 126
School of Medicine, Air Force, San Antonio, 147
Schirra, Walter, 156
Schramm, Gerhard, 179
Schreiner, Dr. George, 88
Scribner, Dr. Belding H., 75, 90
Seattle, Artificial Kidney Center, 85, 193
Severinghaus, Dr. John W., 155
Shelley, Mary, 190
Sherrington, Sir Charles, 93
Signals, myoelectric (EMG), 69–70, 106–111, 144
Siodmak, Curt, 91, 92
Skeleton, 48–51
Skin, electrical potential study, 144
Sleep and brain, 98, 100–101
Socket, universal hip, 74
Solenoid, electrical, 53, 68
Sonneborn, T. M., 188
Space, and cyborg, 18, 146–156
environment, 146
hazards of, 18
man adapting to, 147–156
Space flight and metabolism, 149–152
Spacelabs, Incorporated, 109
Spalding, Dr. John Frederick, 189

Space Merchants, The, 159
Sperm banks, 165, 166, 171
Spleen, function of, 54
transplant, 77
Stanley, W. M., 177
Stapledon, Dr. William Olaf, 36, 154, 199–200
Surgery, artificial organs, 78–90
German, 25
grafting living material, 71–74
internal repair, 75–76
and metal inserts, 26–28
and nose repair, 29–30
and organ transplants, 42
plastic, 16–17
Synthesis of DNA, 179

Tapp, Dr. James S., 80
Teeth, transplanted, 26
Test-tube babies, 165, 167, 168–171
Thalidomide, 63, 124–125
Thalidomide Trust, 108
Thyroid, 32, 149
"Tinkertoy" approach, 74
Tissue banks, 160
culture, 158–162
Toolmaking and man, 11, 22–24
Trachea transplants, 77
Transfusion, blood, 31
Transmitter, implanted, 116
Transplants, 76–78
and immune reaction, 33
lower animals and, 30, 33
types of, 73

UCLA, 62, 111
United Aircraft Corporation, 153
U.S. Army, prosthetics research, 62
U.S.A.F. bionics projects, 140–141
U.S. Navy, bioelectrical firing control, 117
cyborgs, 141–144
prosthetics research, 62

University of California, 62, 65

Valve, artificial aortic, 81
Vasectomy, 164
Veterans Administration, kidney centers, 85
prosthetics research, 62
telemedography, 116
Virus, composition of, 177
Voronoff, S., 32–33, 78

Walking machines, 145
Walter, Dr. W. Grey, 101–102
Wasserman, Walter L., 144

Waste product accumulation, 186
Water, breathing, 19, 142, 155
Watson, James, 178, 180, 184
Weapons, remote control, 138–139, 140
Weil, Professor Sigmund, 66
Weltman, Dr., 108, 109
Whitcomb, Dr. Walter H., 126
White Motor Company, 83
White, Dr. Robert J., 92
Wiener, Norbert, 41, 105, 106, 107, 112

Wilkins, Maurice, 178, 180
Wolfe, Bernard, quoted, 67–68, 111–113, 137
World War I, amputees of, 25
World War II, amputees of, 139
World, the Flesh and the Devil, The, 22, 93, 100, 117, 146–147, 200–202

Yale Medical School, 95
Yesalis, Charles, 69, 107

Zoll, Dr. Paul M., 81

Format by Mort Perry
Set in Linotype Electra
Composed, printed and bound by American Book–Stratford Press
HARPER & ROW, PUBLISHERS, INCORPORATED

DATE DUE

GAYLORD			PRINTED IN U.S.A